PASSIVE SOLAR RETROFIT

PASSIVE SOLAR RETROFIT

HOW TO ADD NATURAL HEATING AND COOLING TO YOUR HOME

DARRYL J. STRICKLER

VAN NOSTRAND REINHOLD COMPANY
NEW YORK   CINCINNATI   TORONTO   LONDON   MELBOURNE

This work is dedicated to *you* and to your efforts to conserve the nonrenewable resources of this planet; and to the children and their children's children: may they always feel warmth.

Designed by RFS Graphic Design Inc.

Published by Van Nostrand Reinhold Company Inc.
135 West 50th Street
New York, NY 10020

Van Nostrand Reinhold Limited
1410 Birchmount Road
Scarborough, Ontario M1P 2E7, Canada

Van Nostrand Reinhold Australia Pty. Ltd.
17 Queen Street
Mitcham, Victoria 3132, Australia

Van Nostrand Reinhold Company Limited
Molly Millars Lane
Wokingham, Berkshire, England

16 15 14 13 12 11 10 9 8 7 6 5 4 3 2 1

Library of Congress Cataloging in Publication Data

Strickler, Darryl J.
    Passive solar retrofit.

    Bibliography: p. 156
    Includes index.
    1. Solar energy—Passive systems. I. Title.
TH7413.S77   697'.78   81-11553
ISBN 0-442-27720-2   AACR2
ISBN 0-442-27719-9 (pbk.)

Contents

Introduction

The sky is perfectly clear on this sunny December morning. A brisk wind is blowing from the north, so it feels much colder outside than the 23° showing on the thermometer. Earlier this morning the local radio announcer advised listeners to bundle up their kids before sending them to school—the wind-chill factor was near zero.

Our house does not have central heat, and even though the temperature dropped into the teens last night, I didn't bother to stoke our only source of internal heat—a small wood-burning stove. I didn't think it was necessary. As it turned out, it wasn't, because the house never got below 69°. Not that I stayed up all night to watch the thermometer; we have one of those that registers the high and low readings.

Where I'm now sitting to write, the temperature is 78°. This particular spot is a bit warmer than the rest of the house because it is a glass-enclosed area attached to what used to be the outside south wall of our house. The sliding door behind me that leads into the main part of the house is open, so that the heat from this sunspace warms the house. If I had been sitting in this same spot last December, I doubt if I would have been able to do any writing: I would have been outdoors—and very, very cold.

What I find most enjoyable about all of this is that I can now look forward to a winter with absolutely no heating bills and a summer without spending money for running air conditioners—even though it gets pretty hot around here in the summertime—and I can look forward to many more years of the same. As soon as I get our wind generator hooked up, we won't have any utility bills at all. In fact, the power company might end up owing us money for the excess electricity we generate.

One of my neighbors, a man in his eighties, came over to visit the other day. I think he really wanted to see how warm our house was. Last summer, while we were rebuilding our house, he would stop by occasionally to see how we were coming along. As I explained what we were trying to accomplish, he often joked about how he was going to save his guest room for us, so we would have a place to get warm when winter came . . . even though he knew we would be finished with our remodeling work by fall.

Anyway, Charlie, my neighbor, seemed a little surprised that it was 70° in our house. We talked about staying warm and other important matters. As we talked, Charlie's face began to show concern over the increasing cost of heating and cooling his house over the past few years and over the cost for this coming year. Using mental arithmetic and, later, my calculator, I figured that Charlie spent nearly $3,000 last year to run his window air conditioners and space heaters. Who knows how much it will cost him this year, or next, or the year after that.

Charlie told me that he had just paid the gas man $210 the other day to fill the propane tank at his house and that he'd probably have to fill it again next month. We talked about how we could add insulation to his house, along with some new windows on the south side, and about how we could enclose his back porch to make a sunroom that would also provide some heat for his house. We talked, but I don't think he heard most of what we were saying. He seemed preoccupied with how he was going to pay the gas man for the rest of this winter . . . and the winters after. So, "The Gas Man Cometh."

When Charlie left, the feeling I had developed as a result of our conversation didn't. I stayed up late that night, and several nights since, not to watch the thermometer, but to think about what can be done to prevent the terrible choice that Charlie and others may someday face or are even now facing—the choice between staying warm and buying food or other necessities.

Sadly, we live at a time when young and old alike are faced with uncertainties that have resulted from our past excesses in energy use and our dependence on conventional fuels, many of which come from foreign sources. On a more hopeful note, however, I believe there are individual choices and actions we can take to do something about this situation. While I am sure not every homeowner can convert his house to a solar house as we have, I am certain most people can alter their houses to make better use of the sun. This not only saves money in the long run, it also provides an example to be followed. I don't know of a better way to help children become conscious of the need to conserve energy than for them to grow up in a home where their physical comfort doesn't depend on external sources of energy being available on demand at the flick of a switch or the spin of a dial. If children can see and live with other alternatives to heating and cooling, they will be better prepared for the future.

At our home the energy future does not seem so dim, because we have taken steps to ensure that we will never be cold—no matter what happens. But we are still concerned for those people who continue to believe the energy crisis is, at best, a bad joke and for those people who are waiting for someone else to save them with a new technological breakthrough.

This book is about personalized solutions to the energy crisis, solutions like the one described above by the owner-builder of a home recently converted to passive solar heating and cooling. The book deals with the measures individual homeowners can use to reduce the energy consumption in their homes through conservation, weatherization, and solarization. In addition to how-to advice on insulation and passive solar retrofit, this book deals with some of the human factors involved.

If you are considering remodeling or altering your house in some way, you probably have specific reasons for wanting to do so. Perhaps you want to add more living space to your house or build a new work area at home so you will not have to spend money for gasoline to drive to an office. Or perhaps your motivation is to save money in the years ahead by reducing your dependence on conventional energy sources. Whatever your reasons, they are personal and valid. You now need to make the decisions and do the planning that will translate your thinking into reality. This book will help you do that.

The book is organized around the steps you will need to follow to achieve the kind of living environment you want. The first chapter makes the distinction between active and passive solar heating and cooling and provides some food for thought in the form of photographs of homes already converted to use the sun more effectively by passive means. Chapter 2 will help you determine the retrofit potential, or "retrofitness," of your current home or of one you may be considering for purchase. The third chapter introduces some of the options for passive solar heating and cooling and will help you to make the most of the retrofit potential of your house. The big question of how to pay for it all is discussed in chapter 4. This information is intentionally included in the middle of the book, not earlier, so you will not allow concern over money to hamper your design efforts. Money is undoubtedly a major consideration for most people, but not having the money in hand should not prevent you from planning what you could do if money were not a problem. In fact, it may not be a problem after you read chapter 4, which contains information on some surprisingly attractive incentive and loan programs for solar conversions. Chapter 4 will also help you decide how much of the actual work of retrofitting you want to do yourself and how much, if any, you want to contract to others. This chapter also contains advice on how to select and work with a designer, architect, contractor, or subcontractors, should you decide to employ any of these professionals. In the fifth chapter, which deals with the actual construction of the passive solar features of your home, you will find much helpful advice and information, as well as illustrations of construction details. And finally, chapter 6 is an "owner's manual" that will help you to get the most from your investment in solar energy. Appendices are included at the end of the book to provide additional information not included in the body of the text.

What you will not find in this book are complicated charts, formulas, or treatises on physics. There are many excellent technical books on solar energy on the market today. This is not one of them, nor is it intended to be. That is, it is not a technical book that deals with solar energy in a theoretical sense. Although it is based on the latest technical information available, this book is written from a practical, rather than a theoretical, point of view.

You also will not find any information in this book on active-type solar energy systems, except for a brief mention in the first chapter. I believe that passive solar has greater potential than active for reducing energy use in homes. Passive solar employs accessible technology and ordinary building materials. The basic principles of passive solar design can be grasped by almost anyone, including children. Once these principles are understood, they can be applied successfully by individuals to their own homes.

The principles upon which passive solar applications are based have been known and used for thousands of years. Perhaps the most notable, and longest surviving, examples of passive solar architecture were constructed by the Pueblo Indians. Passive solar principles were also well understood by Socrates in the fourth century B.C. His writings contain an excellent description of what we would call a passive solar home today. Socrates advocated building the south side of a house higher, to collect winter sun, and the north side of the house lower, to protect it from winter winds.

Do not get the impression that by being an advocate of passive solar I am suggesting a return to the past. Few people today would find the pueblos or the house with its high south portico described by Socrates suitable for their needs. What I—along with many others—*am* suggesting is that we apply simpler, rather than more complex, solutions to our home energy needs.

Perhaps I can make this point best by relating the contents of a phone call I received recently from an inventor who was seeking advice on a concentrating solar collector he was trying to develop. He described his so-called invention as a dish-shaped collector, painted black, with a multifaceted concentrating lens cover shaped like a fly's eye. The collector would be designed to follow the sun through its daily path across the sky and to collect and concentrate enough solar energy to cause water to boil. The steam produced would in turn be used to run a turbine, which would produce electricity for heating purposes. Although this idea is certainly not new, he was trying to perfect it for home use. I naturally offered as much encouragement and advice to the caller as I could, because I sincerely believe that our energy future can be assured only when we have perfected a number of alternative energy forms. What I did not tell him, but feel compelled to mention here, is that I and most people I know would prefer not to have a black, dish-shaped, fly-eyed, self-tracking, steam-producing, electricity-generating, concentrating, parabolic collector around my house. Instead, I prefer a peaceful sunspace and south-facing windows that work with nature to collect and distribute solar energy quietly, without any hardware and its associated complexity, expense, noise, and maintenance problems.

1.

Thinking about Passive Solar Retrofit

What is a passive solar retrofit, and why would you want to "do one" on your house? To develop a basic understanding of the term *passive solar retrofit*, you should be aware of the distinction between active and passive solar heating and cooling systems. The terms active and passive may seem to be a more fitting description of personality types, but in the field of solar energy, they are used to differentiate the means of airflow and heat transfer in solar heating and cooling applications.

Active-type systems used for water and space heating typically rely upon pumps, storage tanks, valves, pipes, fans, absorber plates, and other mechanical and electronic devices to collect, store, and distribute solar energy. Passive systems, on the other hand, rely upon south-facing glass and thermal storage mass, such as masonry or water in containers, to collect and store the sun's energy; and on natural airflow within a building, which results from convection, conduction, and reradiation of stored energy.

The most common application of solar energy for home use to date has been for preheating hot water and for heating swimming pools. These applications frequently include an active-type flat-plate collector system. On a more limited scale, active systems have also been used for space heating in homes and commercial buildings. If you have seen a building or house with what appears to be an array of shallow, glass-covered boxes facing south, you have probably been looking at the most obvious indication that an active-type system is being used, although some passive applications also use such collector devices.

The use of passive solar heating and cooling systems in a structure is not quite so easy to detect, since the building itself *is* the system. Through an appropriate combination of south-facing glazing, thermal storage mass, shading devices, ventilation and natural air movement, and proper site orientation and building configuration, passive solar structures become a system capable of heating and cooling the interior of a building. Passive systems tend to have few, if any, moving parts—other than the people who live or work in them.

The role of people in a passive system is to help the system work effectively by performing functions that regulate heat gain and loss. This usually consists of covering glass areas with insulated shades or shutters at night and on cloudy days in winter, as well as keeping the sun from shining into the house in summer. Thus, passive systems generally require that their occupants be more active, whereas active systems allow their owners to be more passive, since electronic and mechanical devices handle these regulatory functions for them. Most of the regulatory functions required in passive systems can, however, also be performed automatically by mechanical means, such as motor-driven shades regulated by timers or by temperature and/or light sensors, if the owner desires.

Having made a rudimentary distinction between active and passive systems, we can now consider the term *retrofit*, which describes something "fitted" after the fact, in retrospect. For our purposes the fact referred to is the building of your house, and the fitting refers to the application of passive solar heating and/or cooling features.

In terms of your own house—or one you plan to purchase—we are concerned with how to evaluate, plan, design, and rearrange, or add to, the elements of your house so that it becomes more effective in using the sun's energy. In a sense your house is already a solar house if the sun strikes it at all. But it probably does not make use of the sun as well as it could. In fact, the sun may be working to your disadvantage in your attempts to maintain a comfortable temperature range inside your house. Of course, this is not the sun's fault, nor is it necessarily the fault of anyone in particular. Existing houses were built the way they were for a variety of reasons, including architectural styles, neighborhood standards, building practices of the period in which they were built, and more. The ability of the house to use the sun's energy effectively was probably not among these reasons.

ACTIVE OR PASSIVE RETROFIT?

Either active or passive solar heating and cooling can be added to an existing house in a retrofit situation. These systems can also be combined in the same house, resulting in what is called a *hybrid* system. Technically, an otherwise totally passive solar house becomes a hybrid if, for example, a ceiling fan is used to prevent hot air from stagnating at the ceiling level.

Your decision to go with an active, passive, or hybrid system should be based on your own values and beliefs and on what you can achieve in relation to how much it costs, rather than on what others are doing. If you decide to install an active system, you can be more passive in the sense that you will need only to call the best solar heating contractors you can find, have them calculate what they can do, then have the bidder who offers the best deal install his wares on or in your house. If, for example, you opt for an active-type solar hot water preheat system—as thousands of homeowners already have done—you will probably spend $3,000 to $4,000 and you will no doubt have flat-plate collectors installed on your roof. You will also achieve some savings on your income tax and the portion of your utility bills attributed to hot water heating. If this system is installed properly, it may pay for itself in nine years or less, depending upon how fast energy costs increase. It will not, however, keep the people in your house warm if a time ever comes when you can no longer afford to pay for gas, oil, or electricity—or when these conventional sources of energy are no longer as readily available as they are now.

Before you follow the thousands of homeowners who have added active-type solar water preheaters to their homes, you should stop to consider a few other alternatives. First, and most important, a full-scale conservation plan, which includes adding insulation and weather stripping to your house as well as turning down your thermostat and hot water temperature settings, could possibly save you more money in the long run than a solar water heater could, and it would probably cost less in most cases. But let us assume that your house is already well insulated and sealed; what could you accomplish in the way of a passive solar retrofit on your house for the same amount you would spend on an active solar water heater? Perhaps you could add a simple, lean-to-type greenhouse or a more elaborate sunspace to the south side of your house, or you might add some large windows to the south wall and install brick or quarry tile on the floors of the rooms adjacent to the new windows. Maybe your house has a south-facing masonry wall that could be covered with glass or acrylic glazing to make a Trombe wall, which could provide heat to the rooms adjacent to it. Or perhaps you have a porch that could be enclosed with glass to provide a sunny and warm environment on cold winter days.

Many possibilities for adding passive solar features to existing homes are described in this book, and many more are yet to be devised . . . by you. Deciding to go passive does mean, however, that you will have to be considerably more active in making decisions about what you want to do and how to accomplish it. Your area probably has no one you can call who will come to your house and sell you a passive solar retrofit, because such a retrofit cannot be sold in the same sense active-type equipment can be. It must be planned, designed, and built for a specific house and location, specifically for (or by) the people who live in it.

If you decide to retrofit your house with passive solar features, you will not only have the satisfaction that comes from creating something that works in closer harmony with nature, but you will also be assured that your future dependence on nonrenewable energy resources will be reduced.

WHAT DOES IT INVOLVE?

Very simply, a passive solar retrofit could involve as much or as little restructuring of your house as you wish. It might cost as little as $100 to $150 or as much as you care to spend. It all depends on what you want to accomplish by the retrofit.

You might begin thinking about what percentage of savings on your heating and cooling costs you would like to achieve and whether you also want to add new living space to your house. Your thinking on these questions might run along the following lines: "I'd like to save as much as I can and add some living space at the same time, depending on how much it will cost." This approach is reasonable for now, but you should be able to formulate a better answer as you gain more information and explore various possibilities described in this book.

Your retrofit might be as simple as removing carpet from a concrete slab floor adjacent to a south-facing sliding glass door and painting that floor a dark color, or it may be as complex as tearing off the entire roof of your house, opening up the south wall, and building a solarium into the new roof structure. The simplest retrofit options might result in savings of 5 to 10 percent on heating bills, whereas the more complex and generally more costly options could result in 70- to 80-percent savings and additional living space. Be aware, however, that there is not necessarily a direct correlation between how much you spend and how much you will save on heating and/or cooling costs.

As you read further, you should be able to determine the relationship between how much you will need to spend and the payoff in terms of energy savings and/or additional living space. Chapter 4 will help you determine how to pay for your investment in solar energy. That chapter includes information on special mortgage and home improvement programs operated by government agencies and regional electric utility networks such as the Tennessee Valley Authority, as well as federal and state income tax credits and other incentives designed to encourage the use of solar energy for home heating and cooling.

For now it will be safe to assume that, to do a passive solar retrofit, you will need to make some changes in your house and that these changes may result in some temporary inconveniences. You can also assume that these changes will require both time and money. If you subscribe to the notion that "time is money," then all you need is money. If, on the other hand, you have more time than money to spend on your retrofit—and you also have some rudimentary do-it-yourself skills—you will not need as much money.

If you subscribe to the notion that "time spent is money saved," you will probably be spending a great deal of time designing and building. If you do not, you will probably spend a great deal of money having other people do these things for you. Either way, you win in the long run by creating an energy-efficient living environment!

SHINING EXAMPLES

Successful passive solar retrofits have been done in many parts of the world. It may be helpful at this point to look at some examples of retrofitted houses in various sections of the United States. These examples are intended to serve as a stimulus for you to begin thinking about the retrofit of your own home or a house you will purchase in the future. You should not, however, be limited by these examples, since you probably will be able to come up with a unique plan to retrofit your own home. Furthermore, keep in mind that the examples discussed were designed for a specific house, in a specific location, and in relation to the owners' motivation to save energy and increase their living space.

Note: The weather data included in each of the following examples—average temperatures, percentage of possible sunshine, hours of sunshine per year, heating degree days per year, and design temperature—are provided for the

sake of comparison. A detailed explanation of these weather factors and their influence on solar house design is included in chapter 2. The source of these weather data is *Climatic Atlas of the United States* (U. S. Department of Commerce, 1968).

The information on the real estate value of the homes in the examples, before and after the retrofit, and the cost of the retrofit work is included to give you a sense of the economic feasibility of passive solar retrofit. Where an actual appraisal of the property was done, the dollar amount is designated as "Appraised Value" and the date of the appraisal is included. The term "Purchase Price" is used to designate the actual dollar amount paid for the property. "Approximate Value" is used to denote an estimation, by the homeowner or another person, of the value of the home, based on knowledge of the local housing market. Where dollar amounts are not available, the value is noted as "N/A."

The "Approximate Cost" of the retrofit represents the amount the homeowner spent. In cases where the homeowner or a nonprofit group did the construction work, the cost represents the expense for materials only. When a contractor or subcontractor was used, the cost represents materials and labor.

PFISTER RESIDENCE*

Location: (Urban) Minneapolis, Minnesota
Designer: Peter J. Pfister, A.I.A., Architectural Alliance
Builder: Owner-built
Average January Temperature: 12°F (−11°C)
Average July Temperature: 72°F (22°C)
Percent of Possible Sunshine: 56 percent
Hours Sunshine per Year: 2,607
Heating Degree Days per Year: 8,382
Design Temperature: −14°F (−25°C)

Before

Sixty-year-old two-story frame and stucco house; structurally sound but in need of refurbishing. Centrally heated with gas-fired boiler at an annual cost of $750 to $800. Major window areas

*The Pfister residence received a first-place award in the retrofit category of the 1980 Passive Solar Design Awards Competition sponsored by the Department of Housing and Urban Development, the Passive Systems Division of the American Section of the International Solar Energy Society, and the New England Solar Energy Association.

faced north, east, and west. Area: 1,800 square feet (167.2 ca). Approximate value: $65,000.

Description of Retrofit

Styrofoam beads blown into walls, attic insulation added, caulking and weather stripping, 9- by 12-foot (2.7- × 3.6-m), two-story solarium with quarry tile floors, phase change thermal storage rods, and south windows added. Kitchen renovated and other interior refinishing done. Motorized nighttime insulating curtains for south-facing glass and movable insulation for north-, west-, and east-facing glass areas installed. Work completed: May, 1979 to March, 1980. Approximate cost: $35,000 (including refurbishing interior).

After

Heating costs reduced to $250 to $300 annually; 200 square feet (18.5 ca) of additional living space; refurbished and reorganized interior; new kitchen with quarry tile floor. New total area: 2,050 square feet (190.4 ca). Approximate value: $100,000.

1-1. Before: View of south side of Pfister residence (Photo: Franz C. Hall)

1-2. After: View of south side of house (Photo: Franz C. Hall)

STRICKLER RESIDENCE

Location: (Rural) Tulsa, Oklahoma
Designer: Passive Solar Design Service
Architect: Joseph Wilkinson, Jr.
Builder: Owner-contracted
Average January Temperature: 37°F (3°C)
Average July Temperature: 82°F (28°C)
Percent of Possible Sunshine: 65 percent
Hours of Sunshine per Year: 2,783
Heating Degree Days per Year: 3,860
Design Temperature: 12°F (−11°C)

Before

Uninsulated concrete block structure; no central heat: three space heaters, window air conditioners. Average yearly heating and cooling expenses: $1,000 to $1,500. Large metal-framed glass areas facing north. Area: 1,280 square feet (118.9 ca). Purchase price (1980): $60,000.

Description of Retrofit

Old roof completely removed; hollow-core concrete blocks filled with poured concrete to add mass; 8- by 60-foot (2.4- × 18.2-m) sunspace integrated into 60-degree sloping south roof; nine roof windows installed for direct gain and day lighting of interior; outside of walls insulated to R-24, roof insulated to R-32; areas of north glass reduced. Large bedroom, bath, 8- by 32-foot (2.4- × 9.7-m) loft, which serves as an internal sunshade, and attached garage added. Work completed: July to September, 1980. Approximate cost: $45,000. (Owner claimed $4,500 in tax credits on state and federal returns.)

After

Heating and cooling expenses reduced to zero. (Owners cut wood on property for wood-burning stove backup heat.) Solar-heated water from collector fins in sunspace. New area: 2,400 square feet (222.9 ca). Approximate value: $120,000.

1-3. Before: View of south side of Strickler residence (Photo: P. L. Gaither)

1-4. After: View of south side of house (Photo: Darryl Strickler)

BATTLE RESIDENCE

Location: (Suburban) Princeton, New Jersey
Designer: Kellbaugh & Lee Architects
Builder: Collins Associates
Average January Temperature: 31°F (0°C)
Average July Temperature: 76°F (24°C)
Percent of Possible Sunshine per Year: 55 percent
Hours of Sunshine per Year: 2,653
Heating Degree Days per Year: 5,100
Design Temperature: 5°F (−15°C)

Before

Nineteenth-century Victorian-style house with front door facing west; owners needed additional space for growing family; narrow lot running east and west allowed the lengthening of south wall; original house, in good condition, was not altered significantly. Original area: 1,542 square feet (143.2 ca). Approximate value: $110,000.

Description of Retrofit

Passive solar addition (with longest walls running east and west) added to east end (rear) of house; addition includes large family room and small greenhouse on first floor, master bedroom and bath on second floor. Direct and reflected sunlight from clerestory windows (roof monitor) above second floor used for direct solar gain to interior side of massive north wall of addition; breadbox-type water heater built into roof of addition. Approximate cost: $42,000.

After

Heating costs for the house were about the same for the winter before and the winter after the addition was built, despite the 50-percent increase in living space and the increased cost of fuel. Cost of hot water heating reduced approximately 50 percent. Area of new addition: 770 square feet (72.2 ca). Approximate value: $160,000.

1-5. Before: View of west front of Battle residence
(Photo: Robert Perron)

1-6. After: View of southeast corner of new addition
(Photo: Steven Solinsky, SEA Group)

WOLF RESIDENCE

Location: (Urban) Chattanooga, Tennessee
Designers: Ron Wolf, Bill and Susan
    Yanda
Builder: Ron Wolf, Sunspace Construction
    Company
Average January Temperature: 40°F (4°C)
Average July Temperature: 78°F (25°C)
Percent of Possible Sunshine: 58 percent
Hours of Sunshine per Year: 2,591
Heating Degree Days per Year: 3,254
Design Temperature: 15°F (9°C)

Before

Fifty-year-old one-story frame house on a steep south-sloping lot; no insulation. Area: 900 square feet (92.9 ca). Purchase price (1980): $17,500.

Description of Retrofit

House was completely rebuilt: roof removed; second story added; extensive renovation and re-siding of exterior; insulation and interior refinishing; 365 square feet (33.9 ca) of south- and east-facing glass added for direct solar gain to interior; three layers of sheetrock added to interior walls to increase thermal storage mass; exterior decks added to block summer sun from entering house through solar windows; passive solar preheater for domestic hot water installed in roof. Work completed: April to September, 1980. Approximate cost: $40,000.

After

Sun provides total heat required on sunny winter days; wood-burning stove provides auxiliary heat when needed; whole-house ceiling fan cools house adequately most of summer. (House has conventional heating and air-conditioning system to meet FHA requirements, but system is seldom used.) New area: 2,000 square feet (185.8 ca). Appraised value (1980): $68,000.

1-7. Before: View of northeast corner of Wolf residence (Photo: Ronald Wolf)

1-8. After: View of northeast corner of house (Photo: Ronald Wolf)

ALLEN RESIDENCE

Location: (Rural mountains) Albuquerque, New Mexico
Designers: Sara Balcomb and Dr. J. Douglas Balcomb
Builder: Albert Martinez
Average January Temperature: 28°F (−2°C)
Average July Temperature: 73°F (22°C)
Percent of Possible Sunshine: 70 percent
Hours of Sunshine per Year: 3,000
Heating Degree Days per Year: 6,200
Design Temperature: 0°F (−18°C)

Before

Forty-year-old concrete block structure with no insulation; metal-framed windows; no storm windows; heated with propane at an annual rate of 1,100 to 1,500 gallons (5,003 to 6,822 l). (Fuel costs to heat the house had risen more than 500 percent between 1972 and 1979.) Appraised value (July, 1979): $50,000.

Description of Retrofit

Three-inch (7.6-cm) rigid foam insulation board applied over the old roof; new roof applied over insulation; 2-inch (5.1-cm) rigid foam insulation applied to outside of north, east, and west walls, finished with stucco; 8- by 34-foot (2.4- × 10.7-m) combination sunspace/greenhouse built over entire south wall incorporating air lock entry to house and garage. Work completed: July to August, 1979. Approximate cost: $17,200.

After

Use of heating fuel reduced to 250 to 300 gallons (1,137 to 1,364 l) per year; house is warmer in the winter and cooler in the summer than before retrofit. The owner grows most of her own vegetables in the greenhouse. Added area (sunspace/greenhouse): 272 square feet (25.3 ca). Approximate value (September, 1979): $70,000.

1-9. Before: Front of Allen residence (Photo: J. Douglas Balcomb)

1-10. After: Front of house viewed from southwest (Photo: J. Douglas Balcomb)

LEHRBURGER/SNYDER RESIDENCE

Location: (Suburban) Denver, Colorado

Designers: Carl Lehrburger, Solar Technology Corporation; Rachel Snyder, Infinite Energy

Builder: Owner-built, with friends (prefabricated materials)

Average January Temperature: 30°F (−1°C)

Average July Temperature: 73°F (22°C)

Percent of Possible Sunshine: 67 percent

Hours of Sunshine per Year: 3,033

Heating Degree Days per Year: 6,283

Design Temperature: −2°F (−19°C)

Before

Fifty-year-old one-story frame house facing east; no insulation in walls; roof insulated to R-30. Owners purchased house specifically because of its potential for a solar addition. Gas-fired gravity furnace (originally a coal furnace). Area (first floor): 860 square feet (79.9 ca) Purchase price (August, 1979): $61,500.

Description of Retrofit

Prefabricated solar room addition, 32- by 14-foot (9.5- × 4.3-m) Soltec Greenroom™, added to full length of south wall; prefab unit adapted to include kneewall, which houses acrylic glazing panels. Glass doors and windows cut into basement foundation wall to allow sun to penetrate into basement through addition; vents cut in first floor along north wall to allow heated air from Greenroom™ to circulate throughout the house. Insulated quilt material used at night on north, east, and west windows of first floor. Solar addition completed: winter, 1979–1980. Approximate cost: $13,500.

After

Heating expenses reduced approximately 50 percent; solar addition provides most of the heat required for house during sunny days; thermostatically controlled fans prevent overheating of Greenroom™ in summer. Added area of solar addition: 448 square feet (41.6 ca). Appraised value (December, 1980): $75,000.

1-11. After: Front of Lehrburger/Snyder residence viewed from east (Photo: Rachel Snyder)

DEWINKEL/BOONE RESIDENCE

Location: (Urban) Madison, Wisconsin
Designer: Paul Luther and Don Schramm, PRADO
Builder: Environmental Living, Inc.
Average January Temperature: 17°F (−8°C)
Average July Temperature: 70°F (21°C)
Percent of Possible Sunshine: 56 percent
Hours of Sunshine per Year: 2,502
Heating Degree Days per Year: 7,863
Design Temperature: −9°F (−22°C)

Before

One-and-one-half-story structure; light-frame construction with no wall surface facing south (one corner of house points south); minimal insulation in walls and ceiling; centrally heated with natural gas at an average annual cost of $200 to $225 (1975 to 1977). Purchase price (1977): $28,000.

Description of Retrofit

Energy conservation measures begun in 1977; attic and wall insulation added; wood-burning stove installed for supplementary heat; solar addition incorporating living space, screened porch, and working greenhouse built around south corner of house. Solar addition completed November, 1979. Approximate cost: $16,000. (Owners received $1,900 tax credit for state income tax.)

After

Use of natural gas reduced by 66 percent (from 1975 to 1980) through the use of conservation measures, wood auxiliary heat, and solar retrofit (despite the fact that 260 additional square feet (24.2 ca) of living space in the addition were heated and the cost of natural gas rose). Added area (living space, screen porch, and greenhouse combined): 410 square feet (38.1 ca). Appraised value (1980): $65,000.

1-12. After: New addition to Dewinkel/Boone residence viewed from east (Photo: Donald Schramm)

MAGEE RESIDENCE

Location: (Urban) Seattle, Washington
Designers: Tim Magee and Rollin Francisco, Rainshadow Design
Builder: Rainshadow Design
Average January Temperature: 38°F (3°C)
Average July Temperature: 64°F (18°C)
Percent of Possible Sunshine: 45 percent
Hours of Sunshine per Year: 2,019
Heating Degree Days per Year: 4,424
Design Temperature: 28°F (−1°C)

Before

Uninsulated one-and-one-half-story frame house built in 1911. Average annual heating expenses: $1,100. Purchase price (1975): $24,000.

Description of Retrofit

Walls insulated to R-19; ceiling to R-30; infiltration reduced to 3/4 air change per hour; south wall of main floor removed; 250 square feet (13.2 ca) of double-insulated south-facing glass (with insulating shutter system) added; freestanding water storage containers installed behind south glass for thermal storage; some interior walls removed to improve airflow. Work completed: August to September, 1979. Approximate cost: $10,000.

After

Annual heating expenses reduced to approximately $100 through combined effects of conservation, weatherization, solar retrofit, and use of wood-burning stove. Appraised value (1980): $80,000. (Increased value is a result of remodeling and appreciation in market value of houses in neighborhood.)

1-13. Before: South wall of Magee residence (Photo: Tim Magee)

1-14. After: South wall of house (Photo: Tim Magee)

BLUE RESIDENCE

Location: (Rural) Carthage, North Carolina
Designer: H. Nelson Blue
Builder: H. Nelson Blue
Average January Temperature: 39°F (4°C)
Average July Temperature: 77°F (25°C)
Percent of Possible Sunshine: 61 percent
Hours of Sunshine per Year: 2,680
Heating Degree Days per Year: 3,393
Design Temperature: 16°F (−9°C)

Before

One-hundred-year-old farmhouse in poor condition, frame construction, no insulation. Appraised value (1978): $7,500.

Description of Retrofit

Ceiling insulated with R-19 fiberglass batts; walls insulated with R-11 batts by removing and replacing exterior siding; double-insulated patio door replacement glass used to enclose a south-facing porch structure with upper and lower levels; drum wall consisting of sealed 55-gallon drums filled with water (stacked on their sides, two high) placed behind south glazing; fold-down, insulating reflective shutters installed in front of drum wall. Approximate cost: $5,000.

After

House is comfortable year-round and can be left unattended during winter; airtight wood-burning stove and two kerosene space heaters used for supplemental heat; total winter heating costs (1979 to 1980) were $125; summer cooling is assisted with electric fans which cost about $10 a month to operate. Added area (enclosed porches): 256 square feet (23.8 ca). Approximate value: $60,000.

1-15. Before: South-facing porches of Blue residence (Photo: H. Nelson Blue)

1-16. After: Sunspace enclosing south porches (Photo: McKenzie and Dickerson Photographers, courtesy H. Nelson Blue)

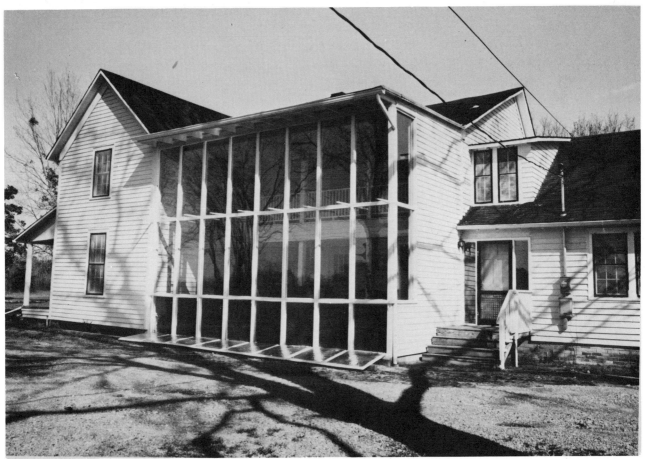

WRENN RESIDENCE

Location: (Urban) Denver, Colorado
Designer: Peggy Wrenn
Builder: Peggy Wrenn
Average January Temperature: 30°F
  (−1°C)
Average July Temperature: 73°F (23°C)
Percent of Possible Sunshine: 67 percent
Hours of Sunshine per Year: 3,033
Heating Degree Days per Year: 6,283
Design Temperature: −2°F (−19°C)

Before

Fifty-year-old double brick house in urban neighborhood. Average annual heating expenses: $360. Area: 1,000 square feet (92.9 ca). Approximate value: N/A.

1-17. During retrofit: Framing for Trombe wall being installed on south wall of Wrenn residence (Photo: Peggy Wrenn)

Description of Retrofit

Forty-seven-foot-long, fan-assisted Trombe wall added to south wall of house; existing double-thick brick south wall painted flat back; double-skinned acrylic glazing used to cover south wall (4½-inch [11.4-cm] air space between wall and glazing); existing windows in south wall serve as vents for Trombe wall. Trombe wall has vents to exterior for summer cooling. South-facing window (not included in Trombe wall) enlarged to provide direct solar gain to interior and provide unobstructed view. Work completed: fall, 1981. Approximate cost: $3,000.

After

Trombe wall is estimated to provide 90 to 100 percent of heat required on sunny winter days and will contribute significantly to cooling the house (cool air is drawn from the north side of the house through the basement and exhausted to the exterior through high vents in the Trombe wall). Wood-burning stove provides backup heat for cloudy periods. Approximate value: N/A.

ZOELLICK RESIDENCE

Location: (Rural) Ada, Oklahoma
Designer: Bill Zoellick
Builder: Bill Zoellick
Average January Temperature: 37°F (3°C)
Average July Temperature: 82°F (28°C)
Percent of Possible Sunshine: 68 percent
Hours of Sunshine per Year: 3,048
Heating Degree Days per Year: 3,030
Design Temperature: 11°F (−12°C)

Before

Mobile home 12 by 60 feet (3.6 × 18.3 m) with an 8-foot (2.4-m) slide-out extension in living room. (Previous owner had applied cedar siding and roof over trailer for aesthetic reasons and built an addition, but did not add insulation. Because of these alterations, this became a non-mobile home.) Average annual heating expenses: $400 to $600. Approximate value: N/A.

Description of Retrofit

8- by 12-foot (2.4- × 3.6-m) greenhouse added to south wall of trailer; sliding glass door installed between trailer and greenhouse; ground-mounted breadbox-type solar water heater built and installed. Work completed: 1979. Approximate cost: $3,000.

After

In addition to fresh vegetables, greenhouse supplies all of the heat required on sunny winter days; wood-burning stove provides backup heat at night and during cloudy periods. Breadbox water heater provides solar-heated water for direct use or supplies preheated water to conventional water heater. The combined cost of utilities for lighting, heating, and hot water totaled $100 to $150 for the entire heating season following the retrofit. Approximate value: N/A.

1-18. After: View of Zoellick residence from southwest showing greenhouse attached to south wall of mobile home (Photo: Bill Zoellick)

KEGEL RESIDENCE

Location: (Suburban) Lancaster,
   Pennsylvania
Designer: Mike Verwey, The Solar Project
Builder: The Solar Project (A Community
   Action Program), Lancaster, PA
Average January Temperature: 30°F
   (−1°C)
Average July Temperature: 76°F (24°C)
Percent of Possible Sunshine: 57 percent
Hours of Sunshine per Year: 2,604
Heating Degree Days per Year: 5,251
Design Temperature: 9°F (−13°C)

Before

One-story concrete block structure; no insulation in the walls; ceiling insulated to R-11; heating with oil-fired boiler at an average annual cost of $400 to $450 per year. Area: 600 square feet (55.7 ca). Approximate value: N/A.

Description of Retrofit

28- by 8-foot (8.5- × 2.4-m) sunspace with insulated end walls and concrete floor added along the entire south wall of the house; east and west walls and the perimeter of house insulated with 1-inch (2.5-cm) rigid foil-faced urethane-foam board, vinyl siding added on east and west walls. Work completed: summer, 1980. Approximate cost: $2,600.

After

Fuel consumption reduced 45 to 50 percent during winter of 1980–1981. Owners use sunspace for living area and to start garden plants. Added area: 244 square feet (22.6 ca). Approximate value: N/A.

1-19. Before: South wall of Kegel residence with sunspace slab poured (Photo: The Solar Project, Lancaster, PA)

1-20. After: Completed sunspace (Photo: The Solar Project, Lancaster, PA)

PETTITT RESIDENCE

Location: (Rural) Carthage, North Carolina
Designer: H. Nelson Blue
Builder: H. Nelson Blue
Average January Temperature: 39°F (4°C)
Average July Temperature: 77°F (25°C)
Percent of Possible Sunshine: 61 percent
Hours of Sunshine per Year: 2,680
Heating Degree Days per Year: 3,393
Design Temperature: 16°F (−9°C)

Before

Late-nineteenth-century four-room house; light-frame construction; no insulation; no central heat. Heated with three to four cords of wood per year. Approximate value: N/A.

Description of Retrofit

Ceiling insulated with R-19 fiberglass batts; walls with R-11 batts; crawl space under house enclosed and insulated. Drum wall, 3 feet (.9 m) high, 30 feet (9.14 m) long, incorporating fifteen water-filled 55-gallon drums added along lower part of south wall. Drum wall enclosure is single-glazed; fold-down insulative/reflective shutters and fan-assisted plenum draw hot air to ceiling outlets in house; cool air returns to the drum wall through insulated ducts in floor joists of house. Attic fan installed for cooling. Work completed: spring, 1980. Approximate cost: $800.

After

House maintains a comfortable temperature throughout the year and can be left unattended without damage from freezing. During the summer of 1980, interior temperatures averaged 78° to 82°F (25.5° to 28°C), while daytime temperatures outdoors ranged between 90° to 105°F (32° to 40.5°C); winter temperatures indoors remain 20° to 30°F (11° to 16°C) above outdoor temperatures on sunny days, without backup heat from wood-burning stove; wood consumption reduced to 1¼ cords during winter of 1980–81. Approximate value: N/A.

1-21. Before: South wall of Pettitt residence (Photo: H. Nelson Blue)

1-22. Close-up view of drum wall (Photo: H. Nelson Blue)

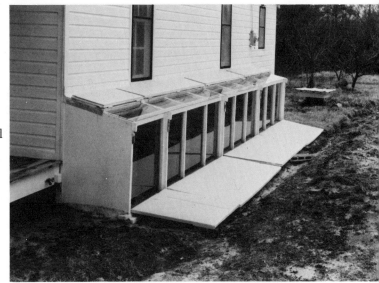

1-23. After: South wall of Pettitt residence showing drum wall and new siding (Photo: H. Nelson Blue)

LEVARDI RESIDENCE

Location: (Urban) Pittsfield, Massachusetts
Designer: Center for Ecological Technology, Pittsfield, MA
Builder: Center for Ecological Technology, Pittsfield, MA
Average January Temperature: 21°F (−6°C)
Average July Temperature: 72°F (22°C)
Percent of Possible Sunshine: 53 percent
Hours of Sunshine per Year: 2,496
Heating Degree Days per Year: 7,578
Design Temperature: −5°F (−20°C)

Before

Small frame house heated with natural gas; 7,422 cubic feet (210.2 s) used during the 1978–1979 heating season. Approximate value: N/A.

Description of Retrofit

Weather stripping upgraded; four site-built 3-by 8-foot (.9- × 2.4-m) thermosiphoning air panels (TAPs) installed on south wall of house. Approximate cost: $600.

After

Consumption of natural gas reduced by 80 percent (to 1,671 cubic feet [47.3 s] during the 1979–1980 heating season). Reduced consumption was a result of milder winter, improved weatherization, installation of TAPs, and conservation efforts by homeowner. Approximate value: N/A.

1-24. After: South wall of Levardi residence with four TAPs installed (Photo: Center for Ecological Technology)

In these times, when our energy future is uncertain, it is comforting to know that, no matter what happens in the political or economic arenas of the world, you can at least count on our side of the planet passing the sun every day. If you live in a house that effectively incorporates the use of solar energy, as the houses in the preceding examples do, you can also count on the sun supplying some of the heating and/or cooling necessary for your comfort.

Finally, if you use the sun's energy passively, you can depend on a clean, quiet, effective, and unbreakable means of heating or cooling your house, which is totally free—after your initial investment—and cannot be metered or shut off by anyone. Now *that's* something to count on!

2.

Determining the "Retrofitness" of Your House

If you have decided to further explore the possibility of retrofitting your house to include passive solar heating and/or cooling features, it is time for some serious evaluation and data gathering. Specifically, you will need to look at the structure, orientation, and thermal efficiency of your house and to gather information on the climate factors of your region, your immediate surroundings, and the exact site on which your house is located. You should also evaluate your own "retrofitness."

After you have read this chapter and have completed the checklist at the end of it, you should be able to decide to what extent you can add passive solar features to your present house.

YOURSELF

The most important criteria for determining retrofitness are personal ones. Before you begin to examine your house, take a look at some of your own characteristics and points of view and those of the people you live with. Are you the type of person who will occasionally take a chance on something if you feel it is worthwhile? Do you believe that the value of something cannot always be measured only in dollars, but at the same time, do you want to make a sound investment in whatever you spend your money for? Do you have the time, energy, and interest to devote to redesigning, and possibly rebuilding to some degree, your own living environment? Do you and the people you live with have a fairly high tolerance for temporary disorder and possible inconvenience in your home if you know it will result in permanent improvement? Do you have at least minimal do-it-yourself skills, and/or could you supervise and direct skilled workers? Does the concept of living in closer harmony with nature interest you? Are you committed to saving nonrenewable energy resources on this planet while greatly reducing your own expenditures for heating and/or cooling your home?

If you can answer an unqualified or even a conditional yes to most of these questions, your attitudes and skills are probably similar to those of people who have already retrofitted their homes to include passive solar energy use. If you cannot answer most of these questions in the affirmative, do not give up the idea; just realize that you may have to make some adjustments along the way.

YOUR HOUSE

After you have completed your self-analysis, you should begin to look at your house. Specifically, you need to consider how it is situated in relation to the sun, how well it is insulated and sealed against the weather, and how and of what it is constructed.

WHICH WAY DOES IT FACE?

The first thing you need to know about your house is the exact orientation of the wall that faces most nearly south. Because the sun is lower in the sky and rises south of east and sets south of west during the heating season, the maximum amount of solar radiation strikes the south side of your house during the late fall, winter, and early spring.

Although you probably have a general idea about how your house is situated, you will have to take an actual compass reading. The type of compass that can be rotated on its attached rectangular base is most useful for determining the orientation of your south wall, since a straight edge of the compass base can be placed directly against the wall or a window. This assures greater accuracy than simply standing in front of the wall and holding a standard round compass in your hand. If you do not already own

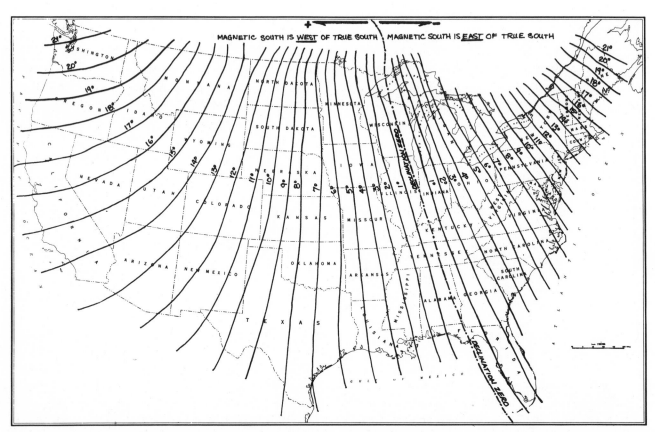

2-1. Compass variation from true south (based on Map #1-1283: *Magnetic Declination in the United States—1980*; Department of the Interior, United States Geological Survey, 1980)

a rectangular base compass, you can buy one for about $5 at your local backpacking or outdoors store.

You need to determine the variation of your south wall from *true south*, the direction of the sun at noon. True south ranges up to more than 20° east or west of magnetic south, depending on where you are located. In other words what your compass shows will not be accurate unless you happen to be along the *Declination Zero* (DZ) line, an imaginary line that in 1980 stretched roughly from the western shore of Lake Michigan to the center of the Florida Panhandle. Magnetic south is west of true south for locations west of the DZ line and east of true south for locations east of the line. You can estimate the number of degrees difference between true south and magnetic south for your location by referring to the map in figure 2-1. Note that the map shows magnetic variations as of 1980.

These variations change slightly from year to year.

Keeping in mind this variation between magnetic and true south, take a reading of your south wall. (If you do not know how to use a rectangular-based compass, follow the instructions and study the examples in box "How to Read Your South Wall.") Do not be too concerned when you discover that your house does not face true south, i.e., 180° adjusted for magnetic variation. Few houses do unless someone planned them that way. If your south wall is even as much as 30° east or west of true south, it will still receive up to 90 percent of the solar radiation it would receive if it faced due south. If it varies by 40°, it receives only about 70 percent of the solar radiation it would if it faced directly south.

In some cases an orientation slightly (5° to 10°) east of south is actually preferable, since

---

HOW TO READ YOUR SOUTH WALL

(with a rectangular-based compass)

1. While standing either indoors or outdoors, with compass in hand, point the "direction of travel" arrow on the compass base *away from* the outside of the south wall of your house.
2. Place the narrow edge of the compass base against the south wall or a window in the south wall. Be sure that the compass is level and that no metal is near it. Avoid placing compass on stud-frame wall.
3. As you continue to hold the compass level and against the south wall or window, rotate the compass *dial* until the red (pointer) end of the floating needle is pointing to N on the compass dial.
4. Read the orientation of your south wall (in number of degrees) on the dial of the compass at the point where the "direction of travel" arrow meets the dial.
5. Adjust for the variation (in number of degrees) between true south and magnetic south for your locale. (See map, fig. 2-1.) If you are

east of the Declination Zero line, *subtract* the number of degrees of variation from the reading your compass shows; if you are *west* of the line, *add* the number of degrees of variation to the reading your compass shows.

Example 1

The map in figure 2-1 shows that for a house located near Washington, D.C., which is east of the Declination Zero line, the difference between true south and magnetic south is about 9°. The compass shows that the south wall of this house reads 210°, so its actual orientation is 201°, or 21° west of south (210° − 9° = 201° − 180° = 21° west of true south).

Example 2

For a house near Denver, Colorado, which is west of the Declination Zero line, the difference between true south and magnetic south is about 12°. If the south wall of this house reads 150° on the compass, its actual orientation would be 162°, or 18° east of south (150° + 12° = 162° − 180° = 18° east of true south).

the house will be warmed by the sun earlier on winter mornings and will face away from the hot afternoon sun in summer. In areas subject to early morning fog or a house subject to shading from obstructions to the east, an orientation to the west of south might be preferable. But regardless of what is preferable, you will either have to accept the fact that the orientation of your house is fixed or pack up and move to a house that has a more south-facing wall. In fact, if you are really committed to doing a passive solar retrofit, you probably should move if the most southerly side of your house is more than 40° from south, since it would not be advisable to use this surface for solar energy collection. But, before you call the movers, consider the possibility of building a wing or addition that does face south, such as a sunspace that overlaps the southernmost corner of your house. Chapter 1 contains an example of a retrofitted house in Wisconsin that does not have a south-facing wall (see fig. 1-12).

A rectangular-shaped house, 16 to 25 feet (4.9 to 7.6 m) wide, with its longest sides facing north and south is usually considered most desirable for incorporating passive solar heating and/or cooling features—especially if the south wall is within 20° of true south and is facing away from the street or access road and/or is shielded from view of neighbors or people passing by. If the above is not a description of your house, however, do not be discouraged. Few things are ever ideal in the real world—including the shape and orientation of houses.

WHAT'S THE LAYOUT?

If your house is two or more rooms deep from south to north, you must consider the current or anticipated used of the areas adjacent to the south wall. If these areas are currently used for storage, utility purposes, a laundry room, or a bathroom, and such usage could not easily be changed, the retrofit might be less feasible than if these south areas were used for living, eating, or sleeping. You could, however, consider a retrofit plan that incorporates clerestory win-

dows to provide direct gain to the north rooms of your house.

Another consideration with regard to the layout or floor plan of your house is its degree of openness. Is it composed of cube-shaped rooms off a central hall? Does it have vaulted ceilings and large open areas? Is it a combination of both types? The issue of importance here is whether your house could be altered—perhaps by adding registers or other openings—to improve natural airflow between areas if it does not have an open plan.

Again, it is important to remember that there are many possibilities for passive solar retrofits described in this book—as well as those you can devise yourself—that are worthy of consideration even though your house may not at first appear to be ideally suited for a retrofit.

HOW WELL IS IT INSULATED?

Do not consider beginning actual work on your retrofit before you have done everything you can to make certain that the sun's energy you collect in your house will not immediately escape through the walls, roof, and floor or around windows and doors. In other words, make sure your house is well insulated and sealed against the weather. If it is not, plan to add insulation and weather stripping before or during the retrofit. The importance of this point cannot be emphasized too strongly: *Do not expect the sun to keep your house warm unless your house has adequate insulation, weather stripping, and caulking!*

Most people seem absolutely sure that their house is well insulated, yet few know how much and what type of insulation their house actually has unless they have installed it themselves or recently had it upgraded. What was considered a well-insulated house a few years ago might very well be considered inadequate by today's standards and is almost certainly well below the standard expected for a solar-heated house. In past decades, when fossil fuels were abundant and relatively inexpensive, insulating a house beyond a very minimal level

2-2.

Approximate R Value of Commonly Used Insulation Materials

Material	Thickness/R Value				
	1″ (2.54cm)	3″ (7.62cm)	6″ (15.24cm)	9″ (22.86cm)	12″ (30.50cm)
Batts or Blankets					
Fiberglass	—	R-11	R-19	R-30	R-38
Rock wool	—	R-12	R-22	R-32	R-40
Loose Fill					
Fiberglass	—	R-9	R-13	R-20	R-26
Rock wool	—	R-9	R-18	R-26	R-33
Poured					
Cellulose fiber	R-4.5	R-13	R-27	R-40	R-54
Vermiculite	R-2.5	R-7.5	R-15	—	—
Rigid Board					
Polystyrene (white beadboard)	R-4	—	—	—	—
Styrofoam (closed cell: blue or tan)	R-5.4	—	—	—	—

was not considered cost-effective. In fact, contractors sometimes did not install any insulation in houses if they were faced with cost overruns near the end of the construction process. Furthermore, many older houses were built before insulation was widely used. Keeping this brief review of the unillustrious history of insulation practices in mind, you should determine the actual type and amount of insulation your house has.

The insulating qualities of commonly used materials such as fiberglass batts and blankets, loose-fill insulation, and rigid board insulation are expressed in R values. R value signifies the material's resistance to heat flow. The higher the value of R, the greater the resistance of the material to heat loss from the interior of the house in winter or heat gain from the outdoors in summer. Figure 2-2 lists the R values of commonly used insulating materials. Once you—or someone such as an insulation contractor—have found out exactly what type and how much insulation you have in your house, use

the chart to determine its approximate R value. To get an approximation of the total R value of a wall or ceiling, add 2 to the R values of the insulation materials on the chart to account for the siding, drywall, plaster, brick veneer, and still-air films that cover the inside and outside of the walls of your house. This means that if the walls or ceiling have no insulation, their R value is approximately 2. If your house is covered with a sheathing material under the siding, add another 1.5 to the total R value.

You need not tear apart your walls and ceiling to find out how they are insulated. You can sometimes estimate the R value of an enclosed wall or ceiling by its thickness. For example, a typical 2- by 4-inch (5.08- × 10.16-cm) stud-frame wall can accommodate a 3½-inch (8.89-cm) fiberglass batt which has an R of 11. If you include the other materials in the wall such as siding, drywall, and sheathing, the total R value of the wall would be about 14.5; if the sheathing material is insulation board such as styrofoam, the total R value of the wall would be about 18 or 19. Although 6-inch (15.24-cm) studs or ceiling joists would accommodate R-19 batts and 8-inch (20.3-cm) ceiling joists could handle R-30 batts, do not assume that, just because your house has 6-inch (15.24-cm) joists, the roof has been insulated to R-19. Take a look in your attic or crawl space if you can, or remove a switch plate or electrical outlet cover from the inside of an exterior wall. That way you will not have to guess.

While you are investigating the insulating materials, do not overlook the floors and perimeter of your house. These areas can be a significant source of heat loss. A concrete slab floor should have at least 2 inches (5.08 cm) of rigid board insulation—which extends down to the footing at the frost line 1 to 3 feet (.31 to .92 m)—around its entire perimeter. The depth of the frost line increases as you go farther north. In some recently constructed houses, the slab insulation may be buried a foot (.31 m) or more underground and run perpendicular to the wall of the house. Crawl spaces, enclosed porches, and basement ceilings should also be insulated if the space beneath them is not heated.

An area that is often overlooked is the wall between the house and an attached garage. Obviously, if the garage is colder than the house, heat from the house will be lost to the garage through an uninsulated wall. True, your car may stay a bit warmer if the wall is not insulated, but if you want to keep your car warm at night, hanging a utility light under the hood is much cheaper and more effective. You might also consider insulating the outer walls of your attached garage—particularly if the garage is located between the living areas of your home and the direction of winter winds. If it is insulated, the garage will serve as an excellent buffer space for the house to reduce winter heat loss and summer heat gain.

The amount of insulation a house should have depends on the climate in which it is located and, for newer houses, on federal, state, or local building codes. Common practices in your area and code requirements do not, however, take into account the fact that the sun will be a primary source of heat for a house. To help

you determine whether you have enough insulation in your house, I can offer the following advice: add as much insulation as the structure of your house and your financial situation will allow. Insulation is probably the best investment you can make in your own energy future, particularly when you take advantage of the income tax credits allowed for adding insulation. Not everyone would agree with this advice, but some of those who disagree are probably the same people who also advised the home-building industry, as recently as ten or twenty years ago, that added insulation was not cost-effective. They may have been correct at the time, but they simply failed to look far enough ahead. It is not likely that your house could be too well insulated. Even a thickness of 12 inches (50.48 cm) of fiberglass insulation (R-38) in a ceiling with a continuous vapor barrier is not too much insulation for an extremely cold climate.

To help you decide how much insulation you want, consult two or three local insulation contractors, or energy auditors, who work for local utility companies or state government agencies. Ask them how much insulation they would recommend, summarize their advice, then increase the recommended amount by 50 to 100 percent if you can.

Finally, with regard to insulation, consider using movable insulation on your windows, i.e., insulated drapes, shutters, or rigid board insulation that is put in place over windows at night and on cloudy winter days. This is usually a necessity in passive solar houses and is discussed in greater detail in later chapters. In the meantime, even before yours becomes a solar house, you could be saving considerable energy and dollars by using nighttime insulation on your windows.

WHERE DOES IT LEAK?

Heat loss in winter or gain in summer occurs in your house as a result of conduction of heat through floors, walls, ceilings, windows, and doors, and because of infiltration losses. Most of us are accustomed to thinking of infiltration in terms of the CIA, but in houses it refers to outside air entering a house through cracks around windows, doors, dryer and rangehood vents, and water pipes that go through exterior walls. To reduce heat loss by infiltration, make sure that all of these openings are properly sealed with a sprayed-in, single-element urethane foam or a good-quality, nonhardening caulking compound such as butyl rubber. Go over the entire house top to bottom and fill any spaces where air or bugs could enter the house.

Most homeowners would be surprised to learn that the entire volume of air inside their house changes completely three to five times every hour. In a really drafty house, it could change as often as ten times an hour. Obviously, the more often the air inside your house changes, the more it costs to heat or cool the air. Such changes are mostly the result of infiltration of outside air through gaps in the surface or foundation of a house and through doors that are opened to enter or leave the house.

One goal of most solar house designers is to achieve a tightly sealed house, one that changes its total volume of air no more than once every $1\frac{1}{2}$ to 2 hours. This is the maximum degree of tightness desirable for the comfort and health of the inhabitants of a house, since some fresh air is needed to keep the air in the house from getting too stale or moist. In a retrofit situation, however, reducing air infiltration to this level is very difficult, so you need not worry about making your house too tight.

Another way to significantly reduce infiltration losses is to add air lock entries to the exterior doors of your house. (These used to be called vestibules, perhaps until a submarine commander installed one on his house and decided to call it an air lock.) Building an air lock is simply a matter of adding another door and its associated framing 3 or more feet (.91 m) from inside or outside of an existing exterior door. Thus, the air lock acts as a buffer zone when people enter or leave the house, allowing the inside air to remain inside. If the air lock is large enough, it can also serve as a mud room or a place to hang coats. An air lock entry will help to reduce both heating and cooling expenses.

Probably only a few people left in this country are not yet convinced of the value of storm windows for reducing heating and cooling costs. You are probably not among these few people, but I would be remiss if I did not at least mention storm windows. So here goes. Storm windows: if you don't already have them, put them on. That is, put them on all sides of the house except the south—unless you plan to change any of the north-, east-, or west-facing windows. South-facing windows are excluded from this recommendation because it is assumed that you will make some changes to the south side of your house.

WHAT'S IT MADE OF?

Now that you have investigated heat losses from your house as a result of conduction and infiltration and you have plans to reduce such losses, it is time to evaluate the actual structure and surroundings of your house to further determine its retrofit potential.

From my point of view, the most desirable house for a passive solar retrofit would be a long, narrow, concrete block house, built on a slab, with no insulation, no central heat, and a rotted roof—assuming, of course, that you could buy it for next to nothing and it just happened to be in a choice location, say on the north shore of a lake with the south side facing the water. Oh yes, it would also have very tall deciduous trees that would shade the roof and the south wall of the house in summer, but not in winter.

Such a house would be ideal because it contains a great deal of mass in the form of concrete floors and concrete blocks, which could be further "massed" by filling their hollow cores with poured concrete after the rotten roof was removed. All of this mass would then have tremendous potential for storing the sun's heat energy admitted through newly placed south-facing roof windows and an integrated sunspace. Furthermore, because this ideal retrofit would be located on a lake, the water to the south would serve as a giant reflector—especially when it was frozen over in winter. The lake would not only bounce the sun into the house, it would temper the subclimate around the house, helping to cool the house in summer and keep it warmer late into the fall. Also, the location of the house on a lake would virtually guarantee that nothing would be built to the south that could prevent the sun from striking the house. And, finally—here's the best part— since the house cost so little, you would have plenty of money to do whatever you wanted to improve it!

Before you dismiss the above as mere fantasy, let me assure you that it is meant to illustrate a few points related to the evaluation of your own home. These points will be, for now, general in nature but will be elaborated upon in later chapters. First, a house constructed of mass (dense) materials such as stone, brick, concrete block, or poured concrete has considerable potential for retrofit because of the heat-storing properties of the mass. This does not mean that a frame house does not have equal potential; it simply means that its potential must be developed in a different way. Second, a house made of massive materials with no insulation is in some cases preferable to one that is insulated on the inside, since new insulation can be added to the outside of the house. This allows the interior of the mass walls to serve as a heat storage medium.

If your house has an ailing central heating system or no central heat at all, you are also in an ideal position, since you will be able to put the money you would have spent on a new heating system to better use for your passive solar retrofit project. And, whereas you may be able to get a loan guaranteed by a federal program to do the retrofit, you will not be able to get such a loan for a new furnace.

One final point regarding the "ideal" retrofit house described above: it is an accurate description of an actual house. But it now has a new roof, an integrated sunspace, roof windows, and insulation. It is comfortable year-round, and, best of all, it has a zero heating and cooling bill. This house, in Oklahoma, is among the examples shown in chapter 1.

Some examples of typical houses might help you evaluate your own house. Although the type of house you live in may not be described below—or even if your house is not a type at all—you should nonetheless be able to learn some things from these examples that will be helpful.

The bi-level, raised ranch, or split-entry, as it is called in some areas (fig. 2-3), has been a very popular house in the past few decades because it offers its owner a lot of living space in relation to its cost, and it is relatively easy to build. Typically, this kind of house has an exposed foundation and is sometimes bermed or at least partially set into the ground. If such a house has an appropriately south orientation, it has considerable potential for solar retrofit, since its lower level usually is enclosed by concrete block or poured concrete and has a slab floor. A sunspace, greenhouse, or Trombe wall, as described in chapter 3, could be easily adapted to this type of house, and the foundation walls could serve as a major source of heat storage when insulated properly.

The tri-level or split-level house (fig. 2-4) typically has three levels, one of which is usually at grade level, whereas one level is dug into the ground and has a second story above it. For reasons similar to those elaborated for the bi-level, the tri-level is a good candidate for a passive solar retrofit. Depending upon how the lowest (below-grade) portion of the house is insulated, it also has the advantage of being sheltered by the earth and therefore has a thermal link with the earth surrounding it. (If you live in a tri-level, you might have noticed that the lowest level tends to stay cooler in summer and warmer in winter.) Finally, if your tri-level has a crawl space under part of it, this could be an ideal place to install a rock bed for heat storage.

One more type of newer house, which is really not a type as such, might be called a contemporary American two-story, if only because it was built recently, is in America, and is two stories tall. The front of the house, shown in figure 2-5, faces due west. Its entire south wall, however, is exposed to the sun and the lower portion of the wall that encloses a family room is constructed of concrete block. The owners of this house, who have suffered through some very high heating bills over the past few winters, are planning to add either a Trombe

2-3. Bi-level house (Photo: David S. Strickler, Strix Pix)

2-4. Split-level house (Photo: Phares O'Daffer)

2-5. Contemporary American two-story (Photo: Darryl Strickler)

2-6. Twenties brick house (Photo: Darryl Strickler)

wall or a two-story solarium on the south side of this house to reduce their heating expenses.

One example of an older house is what might be called a "twenties brick house" (fig. 2-6), even though its actual age is unimportant. It is included here because it represents a type of house built in an era when insulation was not widely used. Thus, what would generally be considered a liability when conventional heating and cooling methods are used could actually be turned into an asset if the sun were allowed to shine into the house in winter and it were insulated on the outside.

I have delayed including an example of a wood-frame house (fig. 2-7) until now to raise the anxiety of readers who live in such houses.

2-7. Wood-frame house (Photo: Darryl Strickler)

A little anxiety is sometimes helpful for completing more demanding tasks, which is what your retrofit project will be: far from impossible but still demanding if you live in a frame house and want to achieve a significant solar savings. By now you might be asking: "If I live in a frame house, should I just forget about retrofitting it?" No! You should be thinking about ways to incorporate waterwalls and phase change materials for thermal storage into your house, since you do not have the obvious advantage of having mass materials included in the structure of your house. You can rest assured, however, that water is a much better heat storage medium than mass materials such as concrete, stone, and brick, and phase change materials are even more effective than water alone. Nor do you need to be horrified by the prospect of filling your house with 55-gallon oil drums or culvert pipes filled with water, since many attractive alternatives to these earlier methods of heat storage using water are now available. Water storage can sometimes be incorporated into existing walls, which can be covered to conceal the storage containers. Waterwalls are described in chapter 3.

WHAT'S AROUND IT?

The surroundings of a house are very important when evaluating its retrofit potential. The matter of greatest importance is its skyspace, the area to the south of your house that is clear of shadow-producing trees and buildings. In order for a retrofit to be feasible, your house should have relatively unobstructed access to the sun throughout the heating season and should ideally (there's that word again!) be shaded from the summer sun either by overhangs above south windows or tall deciduous trees that shade the house in summer but not in winter. The altitude of the sun above the southern horizon at noon on December 21, the winter solstice, ranges from 36° in southern parts of the continental United States to about 18° in the northernmost sections, excluding Alaska. At noon on March 22, the vernal equinox, and September 22, the autumn equinox, its altitude

ranges from 60° in the southern United States to about 42° in the northern states. The altitude of the sun on June 21, the summer solstice, ranges from about 85° in the southern states to about 65° in the northern states. Figure 2-8 gives the altitude of the sun for various latitudes in the continental United States. Use the latitude nearest you to estimate the altitude of the sun at various times of the year in your area. These "solar noon" altitudes should help you determine what portion of the space to the south of your house should be open between 9:00 A.M. and 3:00 P.M. when you consider that the sun's daily path is an arc stretching from east to west horizons. Remember that the sun rises south of east and sets south of west on December 21; it rises due east and sets due west on March 21 and September 22; and it rises north of east and sets north of west on June 21. Obstructions that block the sun from striking your house before 9:00 A.M. and after 3:00 P.M. will not significantly affect the amount of solar energy you can collect.

Knowing the sun's altitude during the four seasons of the year will help you to design your retrofit properly. For example, using a protractor, you can superimpose lines representing the sun's altitude at different times of the year onto scaled section drawings of the retrofitted portion of your house. You can then determine how far the sun will penetrate the house or solar addition during winter and how much of the glazing area will be shaded in summer by roof overhangs or other shading devices. Remember, however, that the sun altitudes given in figure 2-8 represent the altitude of the sun at noon, standard time. The altitude of the sun is, of course, lower before and after noon.

The best way to gather data related to your skyspace, or "solar window," and thus, to assess what part of the south wall of your house the sun "sees" is to observe how the sun actually strikes your house at various times of the day throughout the year. Mark your south wall with a pencil, masking tape, or whatever to indicate where the sun strikes or does not strike. Or, better yet, photograph the south wall at 10:00 A.M., 12:00 noon, and 2:00 P.M. on a sunny day on or about the twenty-first of March or

2-8.

Altitude of Sun (in Degrees) above the Horizon at Noon

Latitude	Dec. 21	Mar. & Sept. 22	Jun. 21
28°N Orlando, FL (28.5) Tampa, FL (28.0)	38.5	62	85.5
30°N Jacksonville, FL (30.5) Houston, TX (30.0)	36.5	60	83.5
32°N Savannah, GA (32.1) Shreveport, LA (32.5) Tucson, AZ (32.1)	34.5	58	81.5
34°N Columbia, SC (33.9) Wichita Falls, TX (34.0) Los Angeles, CA (33.9)	32.5	56	79.5
36°N Greensboro, NC (36.1) Nashville, TN (36.1) Tulsa, OK (36.2) Las Vegas, NV (36.1)	30.5	54	77.5
38°N Richmond, VA (37.5) Lexington, KY (38.0) St. Louis, MO (38.7) Sacramento, CA (38.5)	28.5	52	75.5
40°N Philadelphia, PA (39.9) Indianapolis, IN (39.7) Denver, CO (39.7) Red Bluff, CA (40.1)	26.5	50	73.5
42°N Boston, MA (42.4) Detroit, MI (42.4) Chicago, IL (41.8) Medford, OR (42.4)	24.5	48	71.5

Latitude	Dec. 21	Mar. & Sept. 22	Jun. 21
44°N Portland, ME (43.6) Rochester, MN (43.9) Rapid City, SD (44.0) Salem, OR (44.9)	22.5	46	69.5
46°N Caribou, ME (46.9) Bismark, ND (46.8) Yakima, WA (46.6)	20.5	44	67.5
48°N International Falls, MN (48.6) Cut Bank, MT (48.6) Seattle, WA (47.4)	18.5	42	65.5

September, June, and December. Either approach will be a valuable design tool for helping you decide where to place major solar collection surfaces when you retrofit your house.

In addition to these informal observations of how the sun strikes your house, you may want a professional site evaluation, which graphically plots your skyspace for various times of the year. This can be done by a solar professional, or you can do it yourself with the aid of the many excellent technical books on solar energy that contain sun charts for your latitude. Some of these books are listed in the bibliography in Appendix D. A site evaluation is most valuable for a site that has no house on it. Since you have the distinct advantage of gathering actual data in relation to an existing house, the only real reason to do a sky chart is to convince yourself that your observations are accurate.

Unfortunately, the skyspace you now have to the south of your house is not a right guar-anteed by the Constitution. A new mountain is not likely to appear in the vacant lot to the south of your house (unless you live in southern California), but a high-rise apartment or office building might. And that row of small evergreen trees to the south that you admire so much will almost certainly become a stand of very tall trees before long. The matter of what could happen to shade the south side of your house, therefore, becomes very important.

Several states and cities are now considering, or have recently enacted, legislation on solar access rights. In November, 1980, however, a Wisconsin judge ruled against a homeowner who sought an injunction to stop his prospective neighbor from building a house that would shade his solar collectors. Ironically, the new neighbor also planned to use collector panels, and perhaps this very feature of his proposed house shaded the plaintiff's collectors. (Is there no sympathy even among solar advocates?)

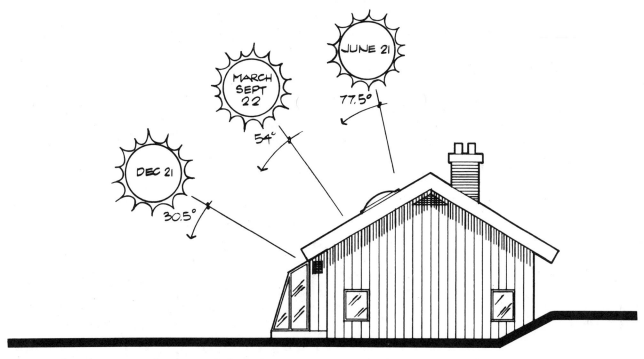

2-9. Sun altitudes at noon for 36° north latitude

WHAT'S THE LAW?

It is a good idea to check state and local ordinances regarding solar access rights or solar easements for your property. In addition, you need to know if any setback restrictions require an addition to your house be located a specified distance from your neighbor's house, your property line, or the street. Local building codes will also affect your retrofit project if they pertain to your property. Find out what they are before you start planning your retrofit.

YOUR CLIMATE

The effects of climate on your house must be considered in terms of both the overall weather conditions of your geographic region and the specific effects of the surroundings of your house on its subclimate.

WHAT'S THE SUBCLIMATE LIKE?

The first thing you may want to consider in relation to the subclimate is the reflectance of the land or water areas surrounding your house. Many colder areas of the United States are frequently snow covered in winter. If you have a sufficiently open, snow-covered area to the south of your house, it will aid the collection of solar energy considerably, especially during the months when it is most needed. Fresh snow reflects about 85 percent of the sunlight that strikes it, whereas typical ground surface area such as grass or dirt reflects only about 20 to 30 percent of the sunlight. Typical urban landscapes reflect 20 to 50 percent of incident sunlight, depending upon the specific location and background.

Because trees affect the subclimate of your house, they can be an excellent natural aid to heating and cooling. For example, deciduous trees to the south, east, or west of your house can provide shade in summer, thus making it cooler; but they lose their leaves just about

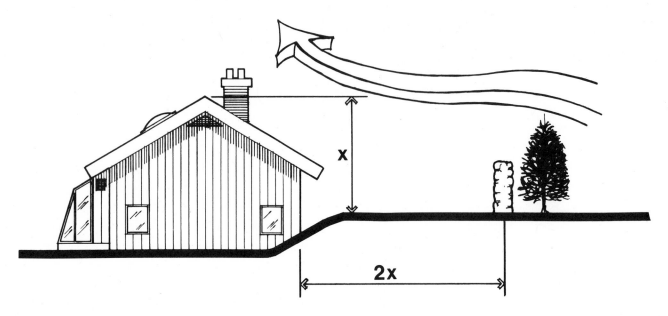

2-10. Windbreak combining evergreens and fence

when it is time to heat your house. (Some varieties of oak, however, do not actually drop their dead leaves until spring.) As long as the trunks, bare branches, or dead leaves do not significantly shade your solar collection areas in winter, deciduous trees to the south are a valuable asset. If they do, you have at least three options: (1) cut the tree(s) down; (2) trim off the offending branches; and (3) design your retrofit to compensate for the shading, i.e., make the solar collection area slightly larger. I do not recommend the first option, since it will probably take you longer to pay off your crime against nature for killing a living thing than it would take to pay for the extra glazing needed to compensate for the shading caused by the tree. At least wait until you see if your solar heating will still work before you remove the tree. You may be surprised to learn that it will and that the shade the tree provides in summer is proportionally more valuable than the heating potential it reduces.

A row of closely planted evergreen trees or tall shrubs, such as arbor vitae, that shield your house from prevailing winter winds can reduce heat loss from your house by as much as 40 percent. You might consider planting such trees or constructing a sturdy fence that allows some wind to pass through it. This will reduce the velocity of winter wind that strikes your house and will help deflect the wind over the house. Such a windbreak should be placed (or planted) upwind at a distance from the house equal to about twice the height of the house. To aid summer cooling, you might also plant low shrubs where summer breezes enter your house, since the shaded areas of the ground around the shrubs will reduce the temperature of the air entering your house.

This next point may be academic since you probably already own a house, but if you ever buy or build another one, it should be located in the middle of a hill that has a 10- to 20-percent slope to the south or southeast. Here it can be dug into the slope on the north and can enjoy an intimate relationship with the earth surrounding it while being protected from north winds and exposed to the southern sun. It will not stand in the open as it would if it were located on the top of the slope, nor would it be subject to the cooler valley temperatures, humidity, and water runoff in winter if it were located at the bottom of the slope.

Alas, since most homes are located on relatively flat land—or land that was flattened to build the house—you will probably have to do the best you can with what you have. So get out there and plant some trees and shrubs in the right places but don't start thinking about pushing dirt up around your house. Earth berming is not a good idea unless you live in a veritable bunker or you are a structural engineer who can figure out how to keep the walls from caving in.

WHAT'S THE WEATHER LIKE?

Thus far you have been considering aspects of your house that you can change. Now it is time to think about those things that cannot be changed but that will affect the design of your proposed retrofit: the weather and climate of your region.

If you have lived in your present area for several years, you have a pretty good idea of what the weather is like. The climate of a given region is determined by summarizing the daily and seasonal weather conditions over a period of years. To assess the effects of regional climate on the design of your house, you will need to find out four specific factors: (1) the coldest temperatures that are likely to be recorded in any given winter; (2) the prevailing wind conditions; (3) the number of heating degree days; and (4) the percentage of possible sunshine. Each of these four factors is discussed below. You will notice a blank after each heading for you to write in the appropriate reference numbers. These numbers will be useful as you begin to design your retrofit.

Design Temperature: _____ °

The so-called design temperature for your house is simply the coldest expected temperature in your area, though not necessarily the record low. The actual temperature in a given area is warmer than the design temperature about 98 percent of the time. You probably already know what this figure should be for your house. If you do not, ask a heating and air-conditioning contractor or call the local office of the National Weather Service.

Prevailing Winds:

Direction: Summer _____

Winter _____

Average Velocity: Summer _____

Winter _____

It is important that you know the direction and average velocity of the prevailing summer and winter winds where your house is actually located. This information will help you plan natural cooling and ventilation for your house and help you decide where to place windbreaks to buffer winter winds.

A large building, a body of water, or a land mass may affect the direction of the wind that strikes your house. So, in addition to checking the maps in figures 2-11 and 2-12—which indicate the direction and average velocity of the wind for the months of January and July—keep an eye (or a wet finger) on the direction of the wind. You might also ask someone who has lived in your neighborhood longer than you have.

Heating Degree Days: _____ DD/yr.

Heating degree days for a specific region are calculated by finding the difference between the average daily outdoor temperature and 65°F (18.3°C), the temperature at which most houses do not need to be heated. For example, if the average temperature on November 15 in a given location were 45°F (7.2°C), the degree days for that day would be 20(F), or 11.1(C). The number of degree days per day are added to produce monthly and yearly totals. These totals are then averaged over a number of years and are used to determine how much supplementary heat a building will need to maintain a comfortable indoor temperature. (The U.S. Weather Service also compiles data on cooling degree days for days when the temperature is above 65°F [18.3°C].)

Heating degree days for various locations in the continental United States range from 500 DD/yr. in South Florida to 10,000 DD/yr. near the Canadian border. The map in figure 2-13

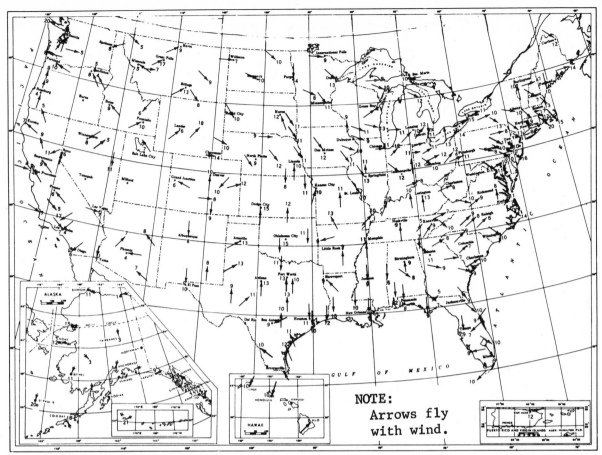

2-11. Prevailing directions and mean speed (m.p.h.) of wind, *January* (Source: *Climatic Atlas of the United States*, Washington, DC; U.S. Department of Commerce, 1968)

2-12. Prevailing direction and mean speed (m.p.h.) of wind, *July* (Source: *Climatic Atlas of the United States*, Washington, DC; U.S. Department of Commerce, 1968)

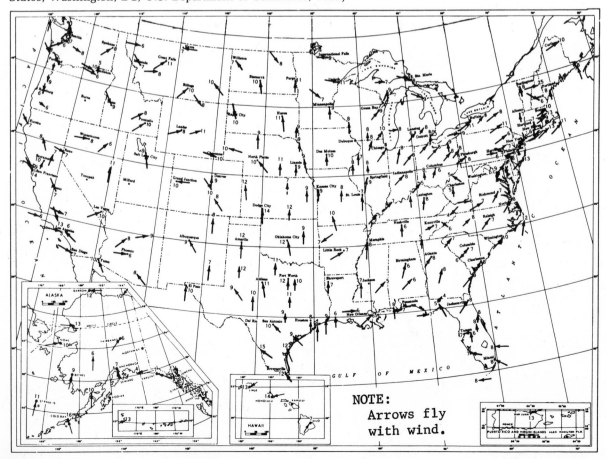

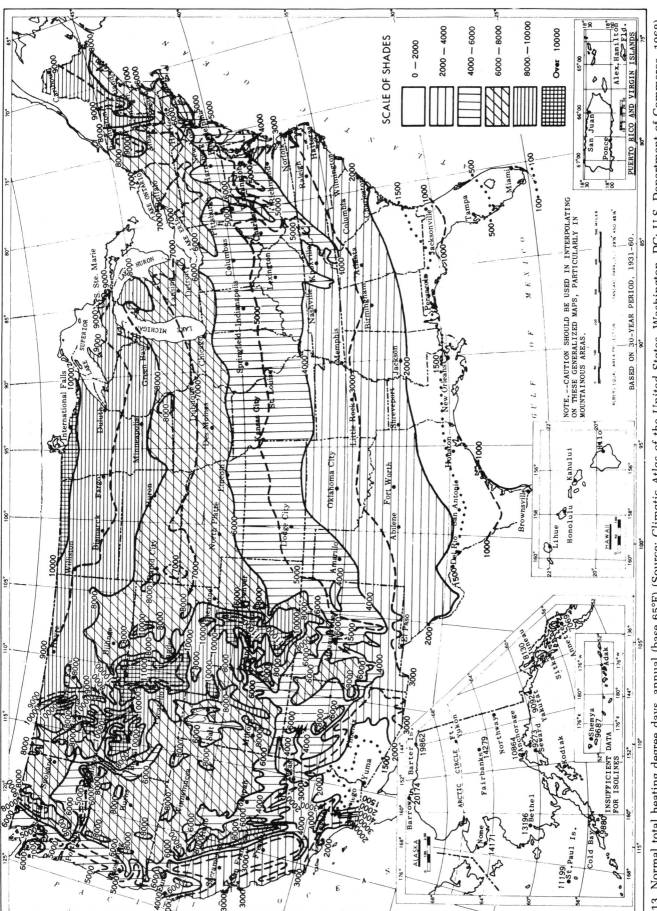

2-13. Normal total heating degree days, annual (base 65°F) (Source: *Climatic Atlas of the United States*, Washington, DC; U.S. Department of Commerce, 1968)

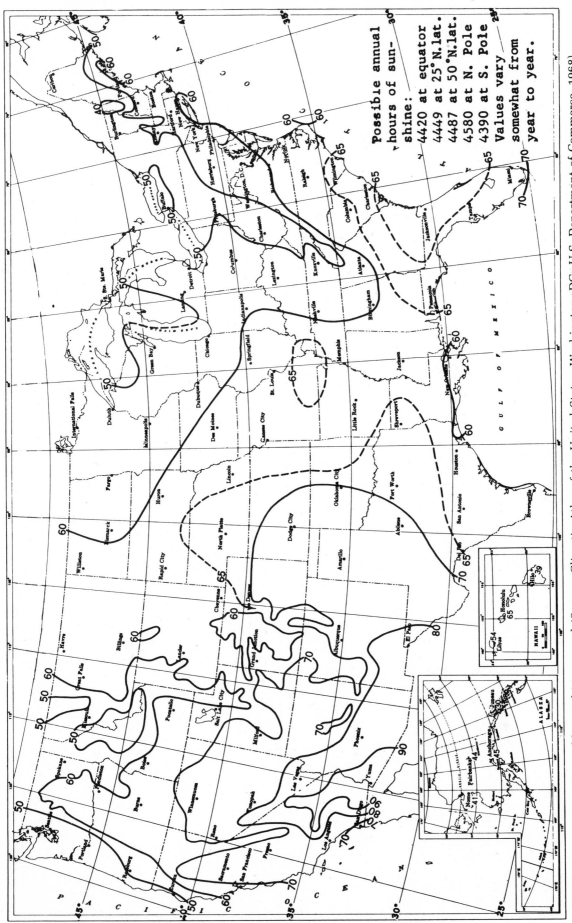

2-14. Mean percentage of possible sunshine, annual (Source: *Climatic Atlas of the United States*, Washington, DC; U.S. Department of Commerce, 1968)

will allow you to make a rough estimate of the number of heating degree days for your area. You can get more exact information from the "Heating Degree Days" chart in Appendix A or by calling a heating and air-conditioning contractor or the local office of the National Weather Service and inquiring about the number of heating degree days for your area.

Percentage of Possible Sunshine: _____%

The next factor of interest in planning the solar features of your house is the annual percentage of possible sunshine your area receives: that is, the percentage of time throughout the year when the sun is actually visible during the daytime. If the sun were never obscured by cloud cover during the day, the percentage of possible sunshine would be 100 percent. Because this never happens here on our planet, we find the percentage ranges from 40 percent in small areas of the mountains of New Hampshire and the Pacific Northwest to as high as 90 percent in areas of the Southwest. Figure 2-14 will give you a rough idea of the percentage of possible sunshine where you live. Keep in mind, however, that this map illustrates yearly percentages. You may live in an area that receives most of its percentage of possible sunshine rating in the summer months, but what is of greater interest is the amount of sunshine your area receives during the heating season. The chart in Appendix A, "Mean Percentage of Possible Sunshine," gives the annual and monthly percentages for selected cities.

OTHER WEATHER DATA

You can obtain much useful information pertaining to the weather and climate of your area by writing or calling:

> National Climatic Center
> Federal Building
> Asheville, NC 28801
> (704) 258–2850, ext. 683

Ask for a copy of the monthly bulletin *Local Climatological Data* for the weather station nearest you. A yearly subscription to this bulletin costs $3.30. You will undoubtedly find it of general interest, and it will be a valuable reference source as you design your retrofit.

SUMMARY

Now that you have evaluated yourself, your house, and its surroundings and have collected some weather and climate information, you should consider this important fact: many people now live in homes for which the sun supplies up to 80 to 90 percent of their annual heating requirements, even though their houses are located in climates with more than 9,000 degree days per year, low temperatures to $-35°F$ ($-37.2°C$), and less than 60 percent possible sunshine. Some of these people live in what were once conventional homes that were subsequently retrofitted to include passive solar heating. Moreover, a number of people living in warmer regions of the United States have combined shading devices and natural ventilation to provide most of their cooling needs throughout the year.

The point is that no matter where you live in the continental United States or southern Canada, you can achieve some degree of savings on heating and/or cooling expenses. Such savings could potentially range between 20 and 80 percent (or higher) depending on where you live, on the type of retrofit you do and how well it is done, and on how well your house is insulated and sealed. All of this, of course, depends on the retrofitness of your house for passive solar heating and cooling features.

The following checklist is provided as a summary of the points discussed in this chapter to help you complete the feasibility study for your planned retrofit. Although the checklist is divided into positive and negative columns, some of the items could be considered either an asset or a liability, depending on the circumstances. Please recall that these are general guidelines, and they may or may not apply to your house.

RETROFITNESS CHECKLIST

ASSETS	**LIABILITIES**

Orientation/Layout

_____ Lowest side (or smallest surface area) of house faces into winter winds.	_____ Highest side of house (or largest surface area) faces into winter winds.
_____ House is at an angle to or faces away from winter winds.	_____ House faces directly into winter winds.
_____ House has only small glass areas facing winter winds.	_____ House has large glass area facing winter winds.
_____ Largest surface area of house faces summer breeze and/or faces south.	_____ Smallest surface area of house faces south and/or faces summer breeze.
_____ House has garage or utility areas located on side of house struck by winter winds.	
_____ Entry doors are located on side of house away from prevailing winter winds or have possibilities for air lock entries.	_____ Entry doors face prevailing winter winds; air lock entries are not feasible.
_____ North and south walls are longest walls of house (long axis of house runs east and west).	_____ Longest walls of house are east and west walls (long axis of house runs north and south).
_____ Angle of south wall is less than 30° east or west of true south.	_____ Angle of south-facing wall is more than 40° east or west of true south.

Skyspace and Surroundings/Location

_____ Tall deciduous trees with high branches, 10 to 15 feet (3 to 4.6 m) from house on south, east, and west.	_____ Short deciduous trees with dense branches or huge trees with thick trunks located 10 to 15 feet (3 to 4.6 m) from south side of house.
_____ Evergreen trees 30 to 50 feet (9.2 to 15 m) from the north or northwest side of house (or side of house facing winter winds).	_____ Evergreen trees or tall shrubs that shade south side of house.
_____ Undeveloped land that you own (or could buy) to the south.	_____ Undeveloped land to south on which something could be built that would shade the south side of the house.

ASSETS	**LIABILITIES**
_____ Tall buildings or other structures located within 30 feet (9.2 m) of north side of house.	_____ Tall buildings, mountains, and other immovable objects shade south side of house.
_____ Body of water or land area frequently snow covered in winter, located to south.	_____ Large expanses of concrete or asphalt located to south.

Structure of House

_____ South-facing portion of house is constructed of masonry that is either uninsulated or from which insulation can be selectively removed.	_____ House is poorly insulated with little prospect for improving the insulation.
_____ House is poorly insulated but would not be difficult to improve.	
_____ House has a great deal of masonry material throughout (e.g., brick, concrete block, stone).	_____ House is of light-frame (two-by-fours) construction.
_____ House is built on a slab that has direct contact with ground or is separated only by a layer of sand and/or rock and has a vapor barrier.	_____ House has wooden floor with uninsulated crawl space beneath it.
_____ House has basement with south wall (within 30° of due south) exposed to the sun, but north, east, and west walls are not exposed or are only partially exposed.	_____ House has cool, damp basement; south wall is not exposed to the sun, or north, east, or west walls are exposed and uninsulated.
_____ House has large areas of glass (or space to add glass areas) facing within 30° of true south; house has smaller glass areas facing north, west, or east; or if it does not, north, east, or west glass area can be reduced.	_____ House has large areas of glass (which could not be practically removed) facing north, east, or west; house has virtually no prospects for adding glass areas on south face, either in walls or roof.
_____ House has open floor plan, e.g., vaulted ceilings, lofts, etc., (or could be adapted to such a plan without the roof caving in).	_____ House has closed-in floor plan, e.g., rooms are separate cubes, which could not be changed without the roof collapsing.

ASSETS	LIABILITIES

Personal Characteristics

_____ You are the kind of person who sometimes likes to take chances, to "go for it."

_____ You seldom take chances.

_____ You have a high tolerance for disorder and chaos and could live with a mess for whatever period of time was necessary to make a permanent improvement in your living conditions and/or reduce your utility bills.

_____ You cannot stand disorder and chaos and could never live even temporarily with a mess.

_____ You are usually among the first to take up the new.

_____ You are usually among the last to lay the old aside.

_____ You do not mind if your neighbors or other people think you are a bit strange.

_____ You are disturbed if other people think you are different.

_____ You do not measure the success or quality of your life in dollars.

_____ You tend to be concerned with how much money you do or do not have.

_____ You would like to save some energy for future generations by reducing the amount you now use to heat and cool your house.

_____ You would like to reduce your own utility bills so you can afford the gasoline you need to take a summer vacation and so you will never need to worry about leaving the lights on when you go out.

_____ You would like to stay at home more often to enjoy family and friends and just relax; in fact, you work at home or would like to.

_____ You like to get away from home as often as you can, even to just go for a drive.

3.

Deciding What to Do with What You Have

By now you should have made a reasonably accurate estimate of the potential you and your house have for doing a passive solar retrofit. The issues you need to consider next are how to make the most of this potential and how to accomplish the kind of living environment and energy savings you want.

A number of retrofit possibilities are described in this chapter, beginning with the simplest and proceeding to the most complex. All of the options presented have been tried and tested for a number of years by researchers and homeowners alike. No far-out schemes or blue-sky dreams are included, nor are there any hare-brained ideas from mad scientists or "solar freaks." Just practical, workable ideas to include the sun's energy in your house—gently.

As you consider these options, begin to think about devising your own retrofit plan. At this point the options are described in general terms, and a means to roughly estimate the cost of each is given. This should help you determine what option or combination of options is best suited to your needs and your financial

situation. Advice on how to design your retrofit is included in the second part of this chapter. Actual construction details of each option are included in chapter 5.

At this point, it's time for a short quiz.

Are you primarily interested in: (check one)

_____ A. reducing your heating and cooling expenses without adding living space?

_____ B. adding living space *and* reducing your utility bills?

_____ C. "going all the way" to rebuild your house based upon a passive solar design?

If your answer was A, you will be most interested in the options listed under Plan A below. If you answered B or C, you will want to consider the information in part B or C, but you should also consider the options listed under Plan A, since these options can be used in Plan B and C retrofits. And, although the options under Plan A are described separately, a combination of these options can be used.

PLAN A: ADD HEATING AND/OR COOLING FEATURES ONLY

1. Enlarging or adding *south-facing windows or sliding glass doors* is one of the simplest retrofit options, since it usually does not involve major changes to the structure of the house or the use patterns of rooms. What it does require, however, is an assessment of the construction techniques and materials used when the south wall of your house was originally built to determine whether the wall can be altered to accommodate new or enlarged glass areas.

If you decide to increase the solar gain by adding glass areas to the south rooms of your house, you will need to make provisions for storing the additional heat received in winter. If you are not interested in providing heat at night to the rooms with south-facing glass, however, you do not have to be concerned with the following discussion of heat storage.

Heat can be stored in existing masonry walls, such as a fireplace wall or an exposed (uncarpeted) concrete slab floor, or in containers of water and/or phase change materials (PCM). PCMs are eutectic salt solutions that change from a semisolid to a liquid state when they are heated by the sun. This melting process greatly increases the heat storage capacity of the PCM, and the stored heat can be slowly released throughout the night or during cloudy periods.

To be an effective heat storage medium (or heat sink), a wall, floor, or container of water or PCM must receive direct sunlight from midmorning to midafternoon during the heating season. Thermal mass in walls or floors not directly struck by the sun will help prevent large temperature swings in a room, but they will store less heat, since they do not receive direct sunshine.

When adding south-facing glass, you will have to devise a means of keeping the sun from entering windows or sliding glass doors during the summer when heat gain is undesirable. If you are fortunate enough to have tall deciduous trees to shade these glass areas in summer, your problem is solved. If you do not have trees, possible solutions include fixed or adjustable overhangs, such as awnings or louvers above the windows, or a lightweight trellis above the glass areas on which deciduous vines can grow, thus blocking the sun in summer but not in winter.

You should also think about how to insulate these new glass areas at night and during cloudy days in winter. A possibility is insulated roll-down shades with a reflective underside, which will do double duty to prevent heat loss on winter nights and heat gain on summer days (see fig. 5-3).

The cost of windows and sliding glass doors varies greatly. Many people consider wood frame windows and doors more aesthetically appealing than those with aluminum frames. Wooden units also have greater insulating qualities, but they typically cost two or three times as much as aluminum units. The best way to estimate the cost of adding south-facing glass is to decide on the exact window or door unit(s) you want and get the prices for each; be sure to get an estimate for having the unit(s) installed if you do not plan to do it yourself.

2. *Roof windows or skylights* can be incorporated into your retrofit plan if your house has south-sloping vaulted ceilings, i.e., ceilings that follow the pitch of the roof. Openings in the roof can provide direct solar gain and can contribute to natural daylighting of the interior of your house. As is always the case, if you want to store the solar heat you gain, the sun will have to strike thermal storage mass, such as a concrete floor, a masonry wall, or water- or PCM-filled containers.

If the room or rooms to which you want to add skylights or roof windows have conventional horizontal ceilings with unused attic space above, you may be able to create light channels so that the sun entering through skylights or roof windows can strike the walls and floors below (see fig. 3-1). This might involve some structural changes that may or may not be feasible for your particular house.

Roof windows and skylights with clear glaz-

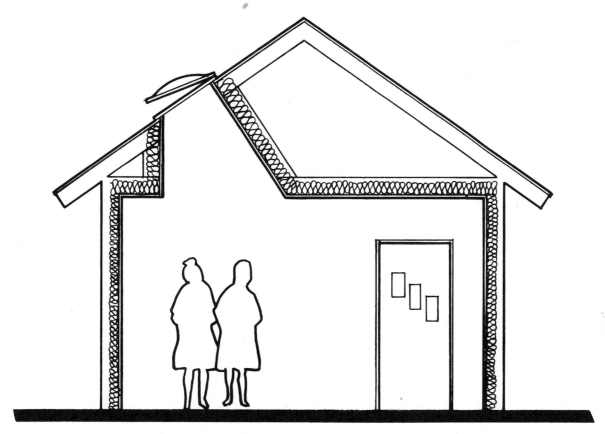

3-1. Light channel for skylight

ing should be used for direct solar gain. Translucent units may be used where glare or fading of furniture or carpeting would be a problem. Translucent glazing transmits slightly less light than clear glazing does, but it diffuses the sunlight and heat energy collected around a wider area of the interior.

Units that open (but do not leak air or water) are usually preferable to those that are fixed because they also aid in cooling a house by providing an escape for hot air that collects at the ceiling level. (Appendix D contains addresses of manufacturers of operable roof windows and skylights that will not leak if installed properly.)

If you incorporate skylights or roof windows in your retrofit plan, you will need to make provisions for shading and insulating them.

The cost of operable skylights and roof windows ranges from $150 to $400 each, depending upon size, quality, and features. Skylights that

do not open cost less but are not recommended, since they cannot be used to exhaust hot air during the cooling season.

3. The *solar collector window* is a relatively new concept that has considerable potential for use in retrofits. This kind of window could replace an existing south-facing window, or it could be accommodated by a new opening cut into the south wall. A collector window consists of two window units, one set to the outside of the wall and the other to the inside. The outer window may be single or double glazed, whereas the inner window is single glazed. A venetian blind—with a dark-colored, heat-absorbing surface and a white, reflective underside—is hung in the space between the windows (see fig. 5-7). In winter the dark surface of the blinds is tilted to intercept the sunlight striking the window. If two double-hung windows are used, the top and bottom of the interior window are left open during the day in

winter so that the heat produced by the sun striking the blinds can flow into the house through the top of the window. Cold air returns through the bottom. The outside window is, of course, not opened in winter. On winter nights the blinds are tightly closed to provide a radiant barrier to reduce heat loss through the window. In summer the white reflective undersurface of the blinds is tilted outward to prevent the sun from entering the house, and the bottom of the inside window and the top of the outside window are opened to provide flow-through ventilation and create a stack effect to exhaust hot air.

If wooden, double-hung units were used, a 3- by 5-foot (.92- × 1.52-m) solar collector window could be built for about $250, more or less, depending upon the specific windows and blinds selected. Aluminum windows generally cost less than wooden windows, but they conduct heat through their frames if they do not have a thermal break between the exterior and interior frame surfaces.

4. The *window box heater* is a viable option in cases where adding new or enlarged south-facing glass areas is not feasible. A box heater is a simple, glass-covered, tightly sealed and insulated plywood box, about 6 to 8 inches (15.2 to 20.3 cm) thick and as wide as the window to which it is attached. It is connected to the lower part of an existing window at a 45- to 60-degree angle. The length of the box is usually determined by distance from the window sill to the ground on the angle selected, minus the space needed to prop the box off the ground. In addition to the single-glazed covering, the box has a black metal or fiberglass absorber plate situated halfway between the glass and the insulated bottom of the box. This allows solar-heated air inside the box—above the absorber plate—to circulate into the house, and cool air from the house to return to the box heater on the underside of the absorber plate. Thus, a thermosiphon effect is created.

A window box heater will supply heat only during the time the sun is actually striking it, since it has no heat storage capacity.

You can build your own window box heater

3-2. Window box heater (Mother Earth News Heat Grabber™) (Photo: Courtesy *The Mother Earth News*)

for as little as $2 to $3 per square foot (.09 ca)— less if some of the materials are scrounged.

5. *Thermosiphoning Air Panels (TAPs)*— also known as solar wall heaters, sun furnaces, passive air heaters, and sun walls—are simple boxlike structures roughly 3 to 4 feet (.92 to 1.22 m) wide, 6 to 7 feet (1.83 to 2.14 m) high, and 6 to 8 inches (15.2 to 20.3 cm) thick that contain a metal or fiberglass absorber plate and are covered with a glazing material. TAPs are similar to window box heaters but are attached

vertically to the south wall and are often used on frame buildings. They provide heat only during the time the sun is actually striking them because they have no thermal storage mass to retain the heat they collect.

TAPs work by convection: sunlight entering the panel strikes the absorber plate, heating the air inside the box. The heated air rises and enters the house through a high vent. Cool air from inside the house is drawn into the bottom of the TAP through a low vent, thus setting up a thermosiphoning effect. TAPs must have backdraft dampers in the lower vents to prevent cool air from the TAP from entering the house at night.

A 3- by 8-foot (.92- × 2.44-m) TAP can be built with about $150 worth of materials. The techniques used to construct them are not difficult to master. There are also several commercial manufacturers of TAPs who produce preassembled, ready-to-mount, or prefabricated units.

6. A *Trombe wall* (or Morse wall) works in a similar way to the TAP described above but has one very important difference: it stores the heat it collects during the day for nighttime use. In a retrofit situation, an existing uninsulated solid masonry wall—or such a wall from which the insulation could be removed—is covered by glass or other glazing material in a frame about 3 inches (7.6 cm) from the wall. (A hollow-core concrete block wall or a double brick wall with space between the two courses of brick could also be used for a Trombe wall if the dead air space in the wall could be filled with poured concrete.) When the sun strikes the wall, heat is trapped behind the glass and enters the adjacent room or rooms through high vents. Cold air from the room is drawn back through low vents into the air space between the glass and the wall. Windows in an existing south masonry wall can sometimes be used as vents for a Trombe wall. (Figs. 5-11 and 5-12 illustrate construction details for a Trombe wall.)

A Trombe wall without vents is recommended if the rooms adjacent to the wall are not used during the daytime—if they are bed-

3-3. Thermosiphoning Air Panels with fan-assisted horizontal airflow; built and installed by the Center for Ecological Technology, Pittsfield, MA (Photo: Center for Ecological Technology)

rooms, for example. Heat travels through an unvented Trombe wall by conduction and heats interior spaces by radiation. The heat traveling through the wall is subject to a time lag of about five to seven hours—the time it takes for the heat generated by the sun to get through the wall—before it can be radiated to the adjacent space. Unvented Trombe walls are less complex than vented ones and are therefore easier and less expensive to construct.

A vented Trombe wall works on the principle of thermosiphon air circulation, and by conduction and radiation. Therefore, it can provide heat during the day and night. As is the case with other solar heat collection devices already described, Trombe walls must have a means to control unwanted heat gain and loss. This can be done by using overhangs that shade the wall during summer and roll-down insulating/reflecting curtains, as well as vents that can be opened to allow hot air to escape to the outside from the top of the air space between the wall and the glass.

If your house already has a south wall made of brick, concrete block, stone, or poured concrete, paint it flat black and cover it with safety glass or other nonbreakable glazing material held in place by a wood or extruded aluminum

vented to the outside. A Trombe wall also makes an excellent sound barrier.

7. *Waterwalls* work on the same basic principle as Trombe walls, except the heat, instead of being stored in masonry materials, is stored in containers of water or phase change materials. Waterwalls are particularly appropriate for retrofitting frame houses, which have very little internal mass. Building a waterwall into an existing south wall of a frame house would require removing the siding and insulation (if any) so that the wall is exposed down to the studs. Several manufacturers offer containers for water or phase change materials sized to fit

3-5. Integral waterwall: Stud Space Module™ being installed (Photo: Courtesy One Design, Inc.)

3-4. Retrofitted Trombe wall with fold-down insulating/reflective shutter (Photo: Peggy Wrenn)

framing system. If, for example, you wanted to cover a 20-foot-long (6-m) section of south wall to make a Trombe wall, you would spend a total of about $500 for five 46- by 76-inch (116.9- × 193-cm) patio door replacement units (double-insulated, tempered, thermopane glass, $50 to $60 each) and the wood needed to build the frames for the glass. At an average cost of $4 to $6 per square foot (.09 ca) of wall surface, a Trombe wall built over an existing wall is perhaps the best value in retrofitting when you consider its ability to supply heat and its ability to help cool a house in summer if it is properly

between studs in a wall. When such containers are placed in a south wall and covered with glazing material, they serve the same function as masonry materials in a Trombe wall. Water-

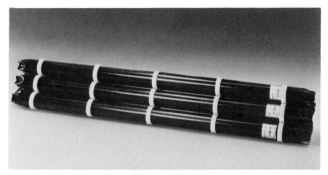

3-6. Phase change materials: Thermol 81—The Energy Rod™ (Photo: Courtesy PSI Energy Systems, Inc.)

3-7. Phase change materials: Kalwall Solar Pods™ (Photo: Courtesy Kalwall Corporation, Solar Components Division)

walls can also be used in the "partywall" between a house and a greenhouse or sunspace.

Water in containers is actually a more effective heat storage medium than masonry materials in most applications because water has a higher density than masonry. The surface of water containers (or a Trombe wall) that faces the sun can be coated with a "selective surface" such as black chrome, which not only increases the absorption of heat, but also reduces heat loss. With a selective surface, the need for nighttime insulation is eliminated. (Selective surfaces such as SunSponge™ can usually be applied in a do-it-yourself situation. See Appendix D for manufacturer's address.)

Phase change materials have an even greater heat storage capacity than water. Containers of PCM are manufactured in various shapes and sizes, including 6-foot-long (1.8-m) rods, 3 to 4 inches (7.62 to 10.16 cm) in diameter, quart-sized (.95-l) metal cans, and fiberglass pods. Any of these containers could be used for thermal storage in a waterwall or in a greenhouse or sunspace.

If you are considering incorporating a waterwall in your retrofit plan, you will need to

3-8. Phase change materials: Texxor Heat Cell™ (Photo: Courtesy Texxor Corporation)

be sure that the structure and foundation of your south wall could support the added weight of the containers. For example, the water and containers in a 16-foot-long (4.8-m) waterwall, 8 feet (2.4 m) high, would weigh about 3,500 pounds (1,587.6 kg). Phase change materials with a similar amount of heat storage capacity would weigh about one-fourth that much.

Manufactured storage containers for a waterwall cost $10 to $20 per square foot (.09 ca) of wall area, depending upon what type of containers are selected. Glazing materials and framing supports add another $2.50 to $5.00 per square foot. Although a waterwall is one of the most expensive types of retrofits, it is also one of the most effective per square foot of surface area. The cost of waterwalls can be greatly reduced by using recycled 5-gallon flat-sided oil cans filled with water and stacked in specially designed support racks behind south-facing glazing.

PLAN B: ADD SPACE AND SOLAR FEATURES

Are you considering a retrofit that will provide not only passive solar heating and/or cooling, but also additional space? If so, you should be thinking about an attached solar greenhouse, sunspace, solar porch, or a solar addition. These all function similarly in terms of their passive solar features, and all are attached to the south wall or corner of a house. The use of each and the approach to designing and building each differ, however.

Although there is no general consensus on the definition of each of these added space passive solar options, some distinctions are made herein to help you decide which will best serve your needs.

1. An *attached solar greenhouse*, or simply greenhouse, as used in this book, is a structure designed primarily for the purpose of growing food and/or plants and providing supplemental heat to the building to which it is attached. It may provide a sunny retreat on cold winter days, but it is not designed to be used as a living space on a daily basis. Because its major function is to provide food and heat, it tends to be utilitarian in design, with less attention given to its aesthetic appeal. This does not mean that it must be ugly, only that its attractiveness is not the major concern.

With the emphasis on function rather than appearance, less time and money for materials and labor are spent for trimming it out. For example, rather than using double-insulated, tempered glass, two layers of inexpensive glazing material—or even polyethylene film—may be attached to the greenhouse framework with rubber-gusseted nails or staples. The inside framing may be treated with a preservative and painted white rather than trimmed with expensive woods such as redwood, cedar, or cypress. And, rather than having a concrete or brick floor, a greenhouse could have an earthen floor with stepping stones between planting beds (*if* such a floor were insulated down to the frost line around its entire perimeter with 2-inch (5-cm) styrofoam beadboard).

The matter of heat storage must be considered when planning a greenhouse. If the greenhouse is attached to a masonry wall, the wall and the floor of the greenhouse will provide some heat storage if properly insulated. In order to prevent great temperature swings between day and night, however, it may be necessary to increase the thermal mass in the greenhouse by using containers of water or phase change materials. Many people use 55-gallon drums filled with water to prevent severe temperature fluctuations in greenhouses. When planning a greenhouse, you must make provisions for preventing heat loss during winter nights and cloudy periods and heat gain in summer.

A greenhouse as described above could be built and finished in one or two days by a local group of experienced "greenhouse workshopers" or in less than a week by a do-it-yourselfer. A rudimentary greenhouse can be built for as little as $100 to $150. Greenhouses built by homeowners or a community-based workshop group usually range in cost from $5 to $10 per square foot (.09 ca) of floor area and are typi-

3-9. Weekend workshop group installing greenhouse (Photo: Bill Zoellick, Sunspace, Inc.)

3-10. Completed greenhouse (Photo: Bill Zoellick, Sunspace, Inc.)

cally 8 to 10 feet (2.4 to 3 m) wide and 12 to 20 feet (3.7 to 6 m) in length. Thus, a 96-square-foot (8.9-ca) greenhouse could be built for $500 to $1,000, depending upon the actual materials used. At that price it's a real bargain, considering what you can use it for. The greenhouse of the same size built by a contractor would cost about twice as much.

A variety of prefabricated greenhouses are available from local and national distributors (see Appendix D). These can be assembled by a homeowner or a local contractor.

2. A *sunspace* might be thought of as the city cousin of a greenhouse. Like the greenhouse, it can serve both food- and heat-producing functions. The major purposes of sunspaces, however, are to provide additional living space, to grow houseplants, or in some cases, to house a hot tub or spa "planted" into the ground. A two-story sunspace is sometimes referred to as a solarium (what's in a name, anyway?). Because sunspaces usually serve different purposes than greenhouses, their owners

3-11. Soltec Greenroom™ (Photo: Courtesy Solar Technology Corporation)

tend to give more attention (and money) to finishing details and appearance. Whereas greenhouses usually have tilted, south-facing glazing,

3-12. Exterior view of two-level sunspace addition by F. Eugene Metz (Photo: Harriet Wise)

3-13. Two-level sunspace addition, interior view (Photo: Harriet Wise)

3-14. Sunspace addition to south wall of west-facing house (Photo: Darryl Strickler)

some roof glazing, and some east- and west-facing glazing to aid plant growth, sunspaces in which growing vegetables is not a major concern should have insulated east and west walls with ventilation openings.

The sunspace is usually conceived as a part of the house—another room rather than a strictly functional appendage. Whereas it might be convenient or expedient to have a dirt floor in a greenhouse, most people would find such a floor undesirable in a sunspace used as a living, dining, or working area. (It would, nonetheless, be advisable to incorporate planting beds in a sunspace just in case you ever want or need to grow food.)

Sunspaces, like greenhouses, must have adequate thermal storage capacity to prevent large temperature fluctuations, as well as insulating and shading features to regulate heat loss and gain. A sunspace usually costs about twice as much as a greenhouse of the same size. For the sake of comparison, you could estimate that a contractor-built sunspace will cost about four times as much as an owner-built greenhouse,

or $20 to $40 per square foot (.09 ca)—depending on how the sunspace is integrated or attached to the house and on what materials are used in its construction. An owner-built sunspace could cost from $12 to $25 per square foot of floor area.

3. A *solar porch* might appear to be nothing more than what used to be called a sun porch, but it has one important difference: sun porches of old were not usually insulated and often lost more heat overall than they gained, especially if they were located on the north, east, or west side of the house.

If you already have a south-facing porch, it could be made to do double duty as an air lock entry and solar porch. All you really need to do is insulate it and enclose it with thermopane glass or other insulated glazing material. Porches made of masonry materials—such as brick columns and concrete floors—are particularly well suited for conversion to solar porches. If you do not already have a porch on the south side of your house, you might consider building a solar porch.

3-15. Glass-enclosed solar porch; installed by the Center for Ecological Technology, Pittsfield, MA (Photo: Center for Ecological Technology)

If you do it yourself, enclosing and insulating an existing porch would cost $6 to $12 per square foot (.09 ca) of floor space, depending upon the glazing you use and the materials you use to finish it. Building a new solar porch would cost about twice that much if you start from scratch and if you employ a carpenter.

4. *Solar additions* is a term that covers retrofits that do not fit neatly into the options described above. Basically, solar additions involve adding to an existing house a room or a wing that has passive solar heating and cooling features. The addition would serve whatever functions you determine—perhaps it would contain a master suite, a family room, a solarium, or a studio. Whatever other functions it serves, it should not only heat itself, but should also be designed to provide supplementary heat or cooling to the original part of the house.

You could get an approximation of how much such an addition would cost by calling several local home improvement contractors to inquire about average costs for remodeling work in your area. These range between $35 and $55 per square foot (.09 ca) depending on what is involved in the remodeling. If you did all or most of the work yourself, you could save slightly more than 50 percent of the cost. A well-planned solar addition should not be more expensive than any other type of remodeling and in some cases could cost less if it is designed properly.

PLAN C: REBUILD

This might be called the "go for it" retrofit plan because it involves the rebuilding of a structure—to whatever degree you desire—to incorporate passive solar heating and/or cooling features. The rebuilding could involve removing the roof, tearing out and rearranging interior walls and living spaces, or adding a second story. And, although this sounds a bit scary to most people, it can be feasible from both an energy-saving and property-value standpoint if—and here's the hitch—if you start with the right structure and a sound retrofit plan. Obviously, such a building should be ideally suited for retrofitting, that is, it should receive high marks on the "Retrofitness Checklist" in chapter 2 and it should be dirt cheap, or relatively so given its location.

3-16. Before retrofit: South porch (viewed from southeast) (Photo: Joe Wilkerson, Jr., A.I.A.)

3-17. South porch and section of roof removed; footing for sunspace kneewall poured and insulated (Photo: Darryl Strickler)

3-18. Rafters being raised for new roof and integrated sunspace (Photo: Darryl Strickler)

3-19. Completed retrofit: Sunspace and new roof with direct gain windows in roof; south wall of original house serves as north wall of sunspace (Photo: Darryl Strickler)

3-20. Before retrofit: View
of southeast corner of house
(Photo: Ronald Wolf)

The term "passive solar wrecktofit" might be appropriate to describe the near total destruction of a house or building that is to be rebuilt as a passive solar structure. The concept of wrecktofit is most feasible if you do not need to live in the structure while it is being rebuilt. A barn, an abandoned one-room schoolhouse, a concrete block utility building, or a small warehouse with loft space in an urban area might be excellent prospects for wrecktofit. If you do decide to purchase a house to rebuild, do not plan to live in it until it is finished. (I know people who tried this; they used to be a nice couple . . . .)

Chapter 1 contains descriptions of houses in Minnesota, Oklahoma, and Tennessee that were almost totally rebuilt, each at a cost of between $30,000 and $40,000. In all three cases, heating and cooling costs were significantly reduced and the market value of the rebuilt house was greater than the total expenditure for the original house plus the retrofit work. Each of these retrofits also involved interior refurbishing, added insulation, and additional living space.

If your present house is not suitable for retrofitting or rebuilding, perhaps you could sell it and find a suitable structure that could be saved from the wrecker's ball and recycled into an exciting new living environment. Following this chapter are several examples that illustrate how nonresidential and abandoned structures could be rebuilt to become passive solar homes.

GETTING INTO HOT WATER

Hot water preheat systems can usually be added anytime during or after the actual retrofit, but you may save time and materials in the long run if you plan to add a solar hot water system while you are in the process of designing your retrofit.

You have numerous options for adding solar hot water heating to your house. You could, for example, install an active-type system if you have $3,000 to $4,000 to spend, or you could spend $200 to $300 to accomplish basically the same thing by using a simple passive system

3-21. During rebuilding: View of southeast corner of house (Photo: Ronald Wolf)

3-22. Retrofit nearing completion: View of southeast corner of house (Photo: Ronald Wolf)

such as collector fins in a greenhouse or sunspace or an integrated or freestanding breadbox-type preheater.

COLLECTOR FINS

Big Fin™ collector fins, developed by Zomeworks Corporation, are simple 8-inch-wide (20.3-cm), 8-foot-long (2.4-m) sections of extruded aluminum with a length of ¾-inch (1.9-cm) copper pipe snap-fitted to their flat black surface. Three or more of these fins are attached in a series to the inside of a greenhouse or sunspace glazing system—or inside south-facing windows—and are connected by a convective loop to a storage tank that is placed higher than the collector fins. As the sun strikes the fins, heat absorbed by the black surface of the fins is transferred to the water running through the pipes in the fins. As the heated water in the fins expands, it rises by natural convection, without mechanical assistance, to the storage tank above. To prevent backflow at night the bottom of the tank should be at least 18 inches (45.7 cm) higher than the top of the fins. (If the tank cannot be placed higher than the fins, a pump is required to move the hot water to the tank.) When the fins and tank are installed in a convective loop, colder water stratifies at the bottom of the tank and is automatically replaced by the hot water that rose by convection from the fins to the tank. Hot water can be drawn off for direct use from the tank, or the solar-heated water in the tank can be hooked up to supply preheated water to a conventional electric or gas-fired hot water heater.

A conventional 30- or 50-gallon (136- or 227.4-l) hot water tank with the heating element removed can be used as a storage tank for solar-heated water if the tank has four openings: two on top, one near the top on the side of the tank, and one near the bottom. A used tank can serve as a storage tank if the water jacket in the tank is in good condition. The storage tank should be well insulated, and it should be covered with an external insulation jacket after it is hooked up.

3-23. Interior of sunspace with Big Fin™ collectors installed inside glazing (Photo: Darryl Strickler)

One 8-foot (2.4-m) fin should be used for every 8 gallons (36.4 l) of water in the storage tank. For example, four fins would be sufficient for a 30-gallon (136-l) storage tank; six, for a 50-gallon (227.4-l) tank, but this ratio may be varied 5 to 10 gallons (22.6 to 45.3 l) per fin. Collector fins should be placed where they will receive maximum sunshine year-round, since hot water is needed throughout the year. Fins can be notched into the mullions as shown in figure 3-24, and the aluminum fin can be rotated on the pipe so that the angle of the collector fin can be adjusted to remain perpendicular to the sun throughout the year. Installing the fins so they can be rotated also allows you to "close" them so they can serve as large venetian blinds if, for example, you need privacy for your hot tub.

The water in collector fins should be in no danger of freezing. (A well-designed greenhouse or sunspace should not get this cold at night even in extreme weather.)

Figure 3-25 illustrates how a simple thermosiphoning collector fin system should be hooked up. (Plans for a pump-assisted system, to be used when the storage tank is lower than the fins, are available from Zomeworks. See Appendix D for address.)

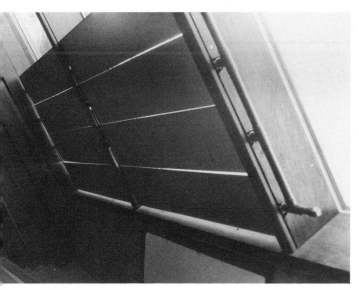

3-24. Big Fin™ collectors in "closed" position for optimum angle to winter sun (or for privacy) (Photo: Darryl Strickler)

BREADBOX WATER HEATERS

Batch water heaters have been in use in all parts of the world for several decades. Breadbox water heaters are a type of batch water heater developed by Zomeworks Corporation in 1974. Although they can vary in many ways, breadbox heaters typically include a boxlike structure containing one or two water tanks painted black. One or more surfaces of the box are covered with glazing material. The box usually has a hinged insulative/reflective cover that is closed over the glazing at night. Breadbox heaters can be integrated either into the structure of the house, e.g., in the roofline or behind clerestory windows, or into a greenhouse or sunspace. They can also be placed in a yard or other area adjacent to the house where they can receive direct sunlight year-round.

Breadbox water heaters are simple, effective devices that can be built by a person with average do-it-yourself skills for $300 or less, depending on the actual materials used. On sunny days breadbox heaters can provide hot water for direct use, or they can be hooked up with a diverter valve to provide preheated water to

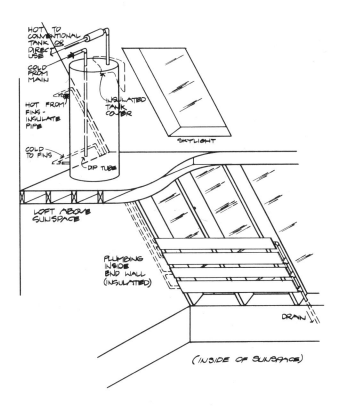

3-25. Installation of Big Fin™ collectors in thermosiphoning mode

3-26. Breadbox-type water heater (Photo: Bill Zoellick, Sunspace, Inc.)

a conventional hot water heating system. Complete plans for building a breadbox water heater are available from several sources (see Appendix D).

DESIGNING YOUR RETROFIT

The process of designing involves the exploration of a number of alternatives in an effort to find the best solution to a given problem. Designing a passive solar retrofit should, therefore, be thought of as a problem-solving process. The problem is how to reduce your home heating and/or cooling costs and, if you desire, add living space. As such, the design of a retrofit is a highly creative and personalized process that can be most effectively accomplished by the people who will live in the house to be retrofitted. This is not to say that a professional passive solar designer or an architect could not do the job for you, but rather that your chances of satisfaction with the completed retrofit will be much greater if you do at least the preliminary planning yourself. You may very well want to have a professional check your work and make suggestions as you get further into the design process. But since you know your own needs, tastes, and financial means better than anyone else, you should do the basic design.

THE 3 *F*s OF RETROFIT DESIGN

The design process you undertake will be affected by three interrelated considerations: function, form, and finances. You should give all of these factors equal weight and consider them simultaneously as you proceed with your retrofit design. If you let one factor, say finances, be your major consideration, you may be setting up an artificial constraint—and thereby encounter the fourth *F* of the design process—

frustration. Similarly, if you give the greatest priority to the form, or appearance, of the retrofit, you may end up with a great-looking but inadequately functioning retrofit. Finally, if function were your only concern, you might build the best-performing, worst-looking, most expensive solar house in town.

The goal of designing a passive solar retrofit is obviously to produce the most cost-effective solution that provides a significant reduction in your heating and/or cooling expenses and enhances—or at least does not detract from—the appearance of your house. If your retrofit adds living space to your house, the additional space should be judged by the same criteria. Does the space fill the need you assigned to it? Does it blend in with the existing spaces and surfaces? Will it lead you not into the valley of the shadow of debt? If you are considering rebuilding a house or other structure, your goal should be to create an appealing and marketable living environment that provides for most of its own heating and cooling needs. The rebuilt structure should also be judged as any other house would be—on the basis of its livability and structural integrity.

THE BASICS OF PASSIVE SOLAR DESIGN

Now that you have considered the process and goals of retrofit design, it is time to consider the basic principles of passive solar design. Once again, these come in a magical set of three: collection, storage, and distribution.

Collection refers to the admittance of sunlight into the living space or other collector such as a window box heater, thermosiphoning air panel, Trombe wall, or sunspace. The key to collection is, of course, south-facing glass or other glazing material in proper orientation to the sun. As you consider collection of solar energy, you must also consider ways to regulate unwanted heat gain and loss through the glazing surfaces.

Storage refers to the materials or medium used to store the heat collected from the sun through south-facing glazing. Thermal storage can be in the form of masonry, water or phase change materials in containers, or other mass materials such as stone, adobe, rammed earth, and even double or triple layers of gypsum wallboard (drywall). To varying degrees, all of these materials will store and release heat *slowly*. And, whereas more dense materials, such as metals, heat up more quickly, they also cool down more rapidly, thus rendering them unsuitable for storage overnight or through cloudy periods.

A corollary to storage is absorption, the ability of the storage materials to attract heat. Thermal storage materials that are in direct sunlight usually work best if they have a dark-colored surface area facing the sun. (The sun does not care what color their behind is.) Nonetheless, dark-painted walls inside the living space in a direct gain application are not recommended, because severe contrast between the wall color and the incoming sunlight causes glare. Dark walls can also overheat. If walls and floors are made of masonry materials, it is usually preferable to have medium- to light-colored walls in a living space and medium- to dark-colored floors. This allows excess heat to bounce off the walls and be stored in the floor. The absorptive qualities of storage materials not in direct sunlight, such as in a fan-forced rock bed or masonry walls not struck by the sun, are not affected by surface color.

The application of a "selective surface" on thermal storage walls increases heat absorption and reduces heat loss from the wall to the outdoors. You might consider applying such a surface to a Trombe wall, waterwall, or around the tank of a breadbox water heater (see Appendix D).

The importance of thermal storage mass within a building cannot be overemphasized. Mass materials not struck by direct sunlight are very effective for reducing temperature fluctuations within living spaces and for absorbing excess heat during both the heating and cooling seasons. Mass distributed over larger surface areas is usually preferable to concentrated mass in a direct gain situation. For example, a 4-inch-thick (10.2-cm) concrete dark-colored floor and 4-inch-thick (10.2-cm) light-colored walls on three sides of a room will function more effectively in most cases than an 8-inch-thick (20.3-cm) dark-colored masonry wall on the north side of the room only. With distributed mass, reradiated heat is spread more evenly throughout the living space, and the ability of the walls and floors to absorb heat from the interior of the building in summer and winter is increased.

Distribution refers to the means of airflow and the movement of heated or cooled air. Passive solar design relies heavily on natural convection, conduction, and radiation as the means of distribution. These require (1) an open floor plan or floor registers and vents so air can flow freely throughout the interior of the structure and (2) thermal mass that can give off its stored heat through radiation to the living space. Distribution also refers to the movement of heated and cooled air as needed to maintain the comfort conditions within a structure. Therefore, it also implies a need for such regulatory devices as roof vents, operable skylights, or rooftop wind turbines to exhaust unwanted heat in summer, as well as for other regulatory devices such as high and low vents in a greenhouse and flow-through ventilation of living spaces. Distribution can, of course, also be aided by such mechanical means as ceiling fans or low-volume fans, which redistribute excess heat from one area to another through an air duct or plenum.

In a practical sense, the discussion of collection, storage, and distribution could be summarized as follows:

<u>If you want the sun to help heat your house, you have to let it shine in, store its heat in (or under) the house, and make sure the heat stays in the house and can circulate.</u>

<u>If you want the sun to help cool your house, you have to keep it from shining in, make sure excess heat can get out, and allow cooling breezes to flow through the house.</u>

APPLYING THE PRINCIPLES

Your task, of course, is to apply these simply stated principles to your particular house. How you apply them will depend in part on whether you decide to follow Plan A, B, or C, or some combination of these.

If you choose options listed under Plan A—adding passive solar heating and/or cooling features only—your task is somewhat simplified, since the options listed under Plan A are already designed to some extent. All you must do is decide which Plan A options you want to use and where they will fit into or on the south side of your house. The collector surface should be placed where it will receive the most direct sunlight during the heating season in relation to the sun's altitude and path across the sky for the months your house requires heating (see fig. 2-8). Moreover, the collector surface should be located where it will be naturally shaded during the cooling season or where external shading devices can be constructed. Once you have decided where to locate the collector areas and what size they should be, you should be able to build (or have someone else build) or install the heating and cooling devices by using the information on construction details in chapter 5.

If you choose options listed under Plan B—adding space *and* solar features—your task is not much different, since solar greenhouses, sunspaces, enclosed porches, and additions are actually live-in collector areas. Again, you must decide how large these collector areas should be and where to locate them for maximum heating and cooling effectiveness. In addition, you need to decide how these added spaces can be tied into and integrated with the existing house; then you can adapt the construction details in chapter 5 to fit your specific situation.

Finally, *if you are going to follow Plan C*—rebuilding—your tasks are to make the rebuilt structure or some part of it a live-in solar collector, so that it can provide most of the energy needed to heat the house, and to make provisions to shade the collector areas and ventilate the house so that it will stay cool during warm weather.

GUIDELINES FOR PASSIVE SOLAR DESIGN

The information presented in Appendix B is included to help you design your retrofit so it will work properly. This section contains specific recommendations and guidelines for locating, sizing, and adapting solar collection surfaces, thermal storage materials, and heat distribution and ventilation openings. As you proceed with your planning, you will find that you need some very specific information. The guidelines included in Appendix B provide this kind of information and should be very useful for reference purposes—if not for bedtime reading.

YOU'RE ON YOUR OWN . . . BUT NOT REALLY

By now you have undoubtedly developed a basic understanding of passive solar heating and cooling, and you should have acquired enough information to produce a viable retrofit plan. The rest is up to you! So get out a sketch pad, some pencils (with erasers), and some square-grid chart paper to do scale drawings. A protractor will also be useful to project sun angles so you can estimate how the sun will strike collector and storage surfaces at various times of the year. Use a calculator and the pricing information in the first part of this chapter to estimate the cost of your retrofit. Do not be concerned at this point with producing architectural drawings of blueprint quality; just sketch out your basic ideas.

You may find it helpful to look through the sketches and descriptions of proposed retrofits included in the pages that follow. These cover a wide variety of homes and other structures suitable for passive solar retrofit. If you can buy one of the structures pictured on the following pages, your plans are already completed. If you can't, perhaps you will get some ideas you can use on your present house.

Consider the Possibilities

THE PHOENIX

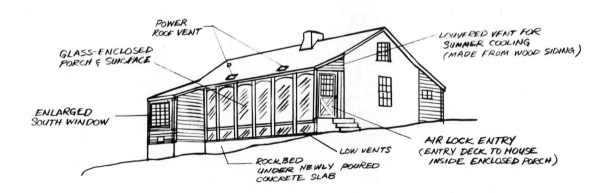

POWER
ROOF VENT

GLASS-ENCLOSED
PORCH & SUNSPACE

LOUVERED VENT FOR
SUMMER COOLING
(MADE FROM WOOD SIDING)

ENLARGED
SOUTH WINDOW

LOW VENTS

ROCKBED
UNDER NEWLY POURED
CONCRETE SLAB

AIR LOCK ENTRY
(ENTRY DECK TO HOUSE
INSIDE ENCLOSED PORCH)

SMALL CHANGE

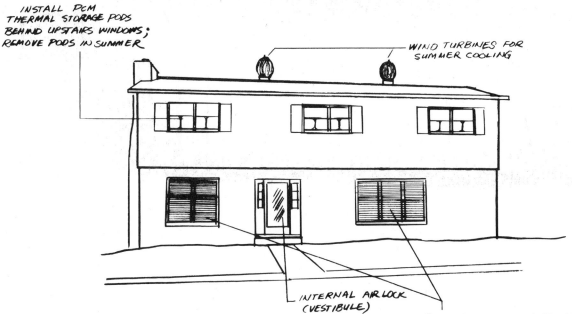

INSTALL PCM
THERMAL STORAGE PODS
BEHIND UPSTAIRS WINDOWS;
REMOVE PODS IN SUMMER

WIND TURBINES FOR
SUMMER COOLING

INTERNAL AIRLOCK
(VESTIBULE)

SOLAR COLLECTOR WINDOWS
MOVE EXISTING WINDOWS TO OUTSIDE
OF WALL SURFACE; INSTALL MATCHING
WINDOWS ON INSIDE SURFACE OF WALL;
HANG VENETIAN BLIND BETWEEN
WINDOWS

VICTORIOUS VICTORIAN

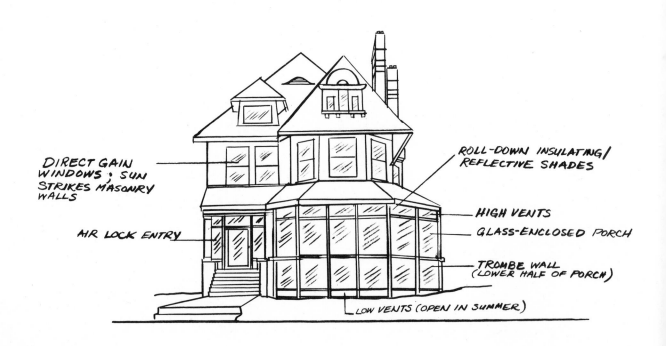

DIRECT GAIN
WINDOWS ; SUN
STRIKES MASONRY
WALLS

AIR LOCK ENTRY

ROLL-DOWN INSULATING/
REFLECTIVE SHADES

HIGH VENTS

GLASS-ENCLOSED PORCH

TROMBE WALL
(LOWER HALF OF PORCH)

LOW VENTS (OPEN IN SUMMER)

SHINE-IN

INSTALL WHOLE-HOUSE ATTIC FAN FOR SUMMER COOLING

OPEN SHADES & REMOVE SCREENS DURING HEATING SEASON

GLAZE SOUTH & WEST WALLS OF SUNPORCH; BUILD SOLID, INSULATED NORTH WALL

PLACE PCM THERMAL STORAGE RODS ALONG NORTH WALL OF SOUTH ROOMS OF HOUSE

BUILD INTERNAL AIR LOCK ENTRY (VESTIBULE)

TRANSFARMATION

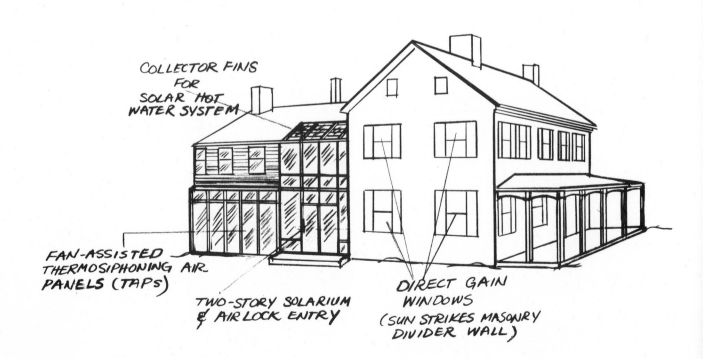

COLLECTOR FINS
FOR
SOLAR HOT
WATER SYSTEM

FAN-ASSISTED
THERMOSIPHONING AIR
PANELS (TAPS)

TWO-STORY SOLARIUM
& AIR LOCK ENTRY

DIRECT GAIN
WINDOWS
(SUN STRIKES MASONRY
DIVIDER WALL)

SPLIT PERSONALITY

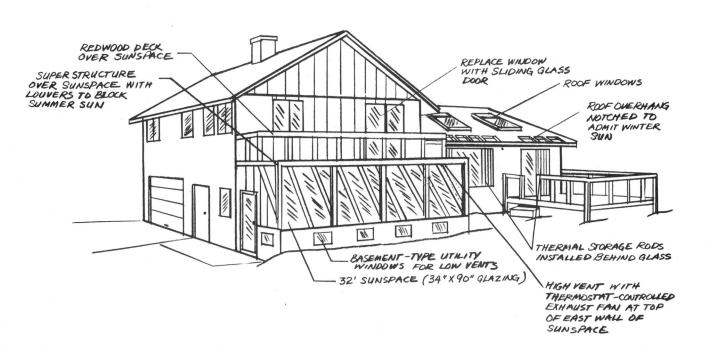

REDWOOD DECK
OVER SUNSPACE

SUPER STRUCTURE
OVER SUNSPACE WITH
LOUVERS TO BLOCK
SUMMER SUN

REPLACE WINDOW
WITH SLIDING GLASS
DOOR

ROOF WINDOWS

ROOF OVERHANG
NOTCHED TO
ADMIT WINTER
SUN

BASEMENT-TYPE UTILITY
WINDOWS FOR LOW VENTS

32' SUNSPACE (34"X90" GLAZING)

THERMAL STORAGE RODS
INSTALLED BEHIND GLASS

HIGH VENT WITH
THERMOSTAT-CONTROLLED
EXHAUST FAN AT TOP
OF EAST WALL OF
SUNSPACE

SUBURBANITE

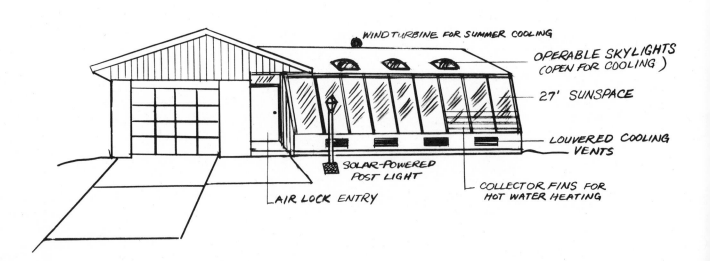

WIND TURBINE FOR SUMMER COOLING

OPERABLE SKYLIGHTS
(OPEN FOR COOLING)

27' SUNSPACE

LOUVERED COOLING
VENTS

COLLECTOR FINS FOR
HOT WATER HEATING

SOLAR-POWERED
POST LIGHT

AIR LOCK ENTRY

MOUNTAIN RETREAT

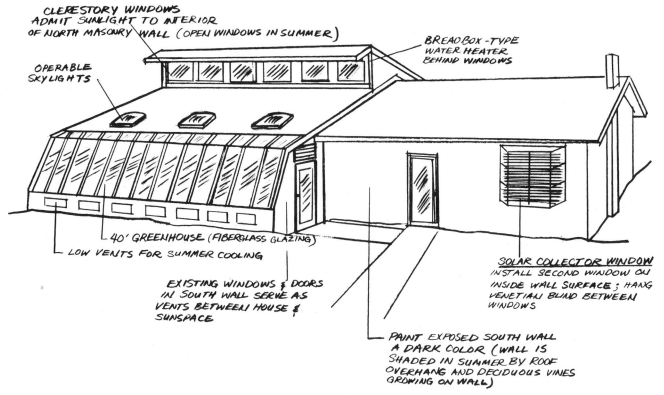

CLERESTORY WINDOWS
ADMIT SUNLIGHT TO INTERIOR
OF NORTH MASONRY WALL (OPEN WINDOWS IN SUMMER)

OPERABLE
SKYLIGHTS

BREADBOX-TYPE
WATER HEATER
BEHIND WINDOWS

40' GREENHOUSE (FIBERGLASS GLAZING)

LOW VENTS FOR SUMMER COOLING

EXISTING WINDOWS & DOORS
IN SOUTH WALL SERVE AS
VENTS BETWEEN HOUSE &
SUNSPACE

SOLAR COLLECTOR WINDOW
INSTALL SECOND WINDOW ON
INSIDE WALL SURFACE; HANG
VENETIAN BLIND BETWEEN
WINDOWS

PAINT EXPOSED SOUTH WALL
A DARK COLOR (WALL IS
SHADED IN SUMMER BY ROOF
OVERHANG AND DECIDUOUS VINES
GROWING ON WALL)

BARN AGAIN

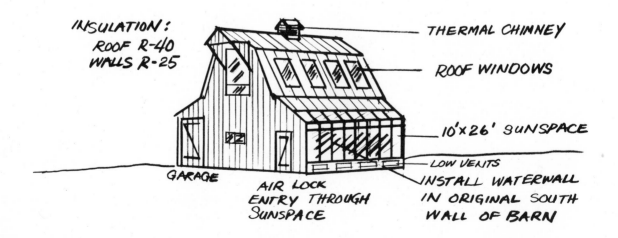

INSULATION:
ROOF R-40
WALLS R-25

THERMAL CHIMNEY

ROOF WINDOWS

10'x26' SUNSPACE

LOW VENTS

INSTALL WATERWALL
IN ORIGINAL SOUTH
WALL OF BARN

GARAGE

AIR LOCK
ENTRY THROUGH
SUNSPACE

TWO-STORY STORY

SUMMER
COOLING VENTS

THERMOSIPHONING
AIR PANELS OVER
FRAME WALL

UNVENTED TROMBE
WALL OVER
FOUNDATION WALL

CITY CO-OP

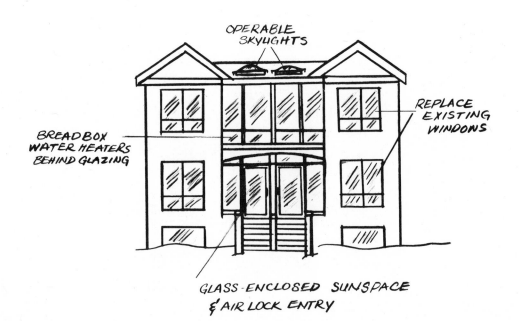

OPERABLE
SKYLIGHTS

REPLACE
EXISTING
WINDOWS

BREADBOX
WATER HEATERS
BEHIND GLAZING

GLASS-ENCLOSED SUNSPACE
& AIR LOCK ENTRY

HACIENDA SOLARO

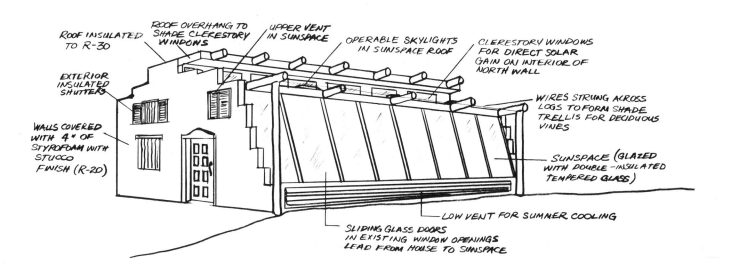

ROOF INSULATED TO R-30

ROOF OVERHANG TO SHADE CLERESTORY WINDOWS

UPPER VENT IN SUNSPACE

OPERABLE SKYLIGHTS IN SUNSPACE ROOF

CLERESTORY WINDOWS FOR DIRECT SOLAR GAIN ON INTERIOR OF NORTH WALL

EXTERIOR INSULATED SHUTTERS

WIRES STRUNG ACROSS LOGS TO FORM SHADE TRELLIS FOR DECIDUOUS VINES

WALLS COVERED WITH 4" OF STYROFOAM WITH STUCCO FINISH (R-20)

SUNSPACE (GLAZED WITH DOUBLE-INSULATED TEMPERED GLASS)

LOW VENT FOR SUMMER COOLING

SLIDING GLASS DOORS IN EXISTING WINDOW OPENINGS LEAD FROM HOUSE TO SUNSPACE

4.

Getting the Help You Need

Hundreds of homeowners in all parts of the country have worked entirely on their own to design and construct passive solar retrofits— sometimes because they could not find anyone to help them and sometimes because they did not need any help. Hundreds more have completed retrofits with the assistance of design professionals or architects, lending institutions, and building-trades people. As you proceed with your retrofit, you will undoubtedly discover that knowing *when* you need help is as important to the success of your project as knowing *what* kind of help you need and *where* to find it.

This chapter is devoted to the when, what, and where of getting help with your retrofit project. It contains advice on legal matters and income tax, as well as suggestions and other information you may need to complete your retrofit. The organization of the chapter corresponds to the steps to be followed in completing the planning and design efforts and making arrangements to begin constructing a retrofit.

Completing a retrofit can become somewhat bewildering at times. The chart in figure 4-1, "The Great Retrofit Steeplechase," is provided to help you along the way and to assist you in evaluating your progress. Should you ever become lost, find where you are on the chart at that moment and follow the arrows that point the direction from there. There are many decisions to make in The Great Retrofit Steeplechase, and you always have the option of backing out. It is assumed, however, that no matter where you are at any given moment in the retrofit process, your goal is to win the steeplechase by making your home more energy efficient and thereby live happily ever after. The numbers in the first box of each row on the chart refer to chapters in the book where information pertaining to the steps in that row can be found.

PLANNING AND DESIGN SERVICES

If you need assistance with the design of your retrofit, you should contact a person who has had experience in this area. Obviously, this person should be someone in whom you can place confidence and whose previous work is available for your inspection.

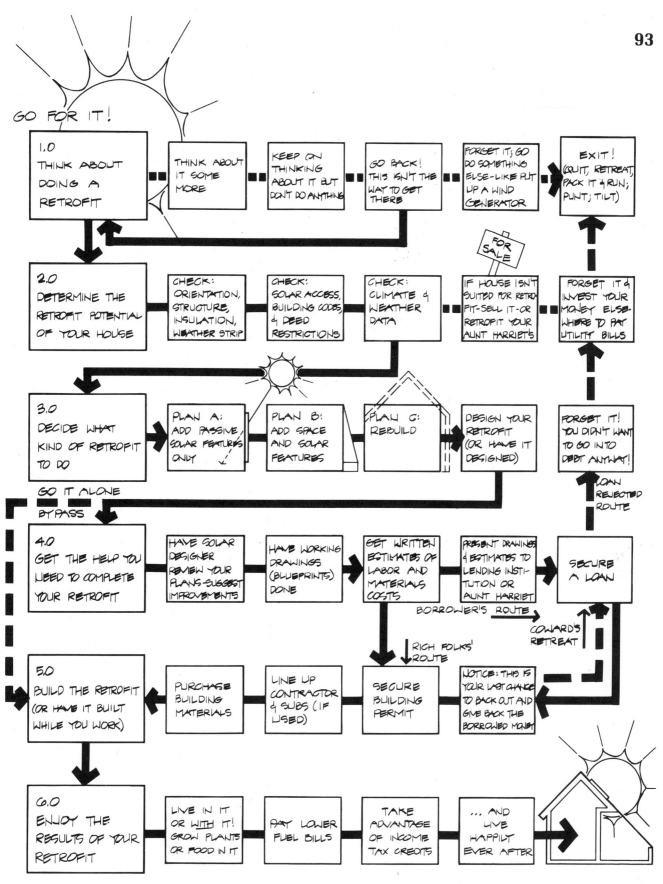

GO FOR IT!

1.0 THINK ABOUT DOING A RETROFIT	THINK ABOUT IT SOME MORE	KEEP ON THINKING ABOUT IT BUT DON'T DO ANYTHING	GO BACK! THIS ISN'T THE WAY TO GET THERE	FORGET IT; GO DO SOMETHING ELSE-LIKE PUT UP A WIND GENERATOR	EXIT! (QUIT; RETREAT; PACK IT & RUN; PUNT; TILT)

FOR SALE

2.0 DETERMINE THE RETROFIT POTENTIAL OF YOUR HOUSE	CHECK: ORIENTATION, STRUCTURE, INSULATION, WEATHER STRIP	CHECK: SOLAR ACCESS, BUILDING CODES, & DEED RESTRICTIONS	CHECK: CLIMATE & WEATHER DATA	IF HOUSE ISN'T SUITED FOR RETRO FIT-SELL IT-OR RETROFIT YOUR AUNT HARRIET'S	FORGET IT & INVEST YOUR MONEY ELSE-WHERE TO PAY UTILITY BILLS

3.0 DECIDE WHAT KIND OF RETROFIT TO DO	PLAN A: ADD PASSIVE SOLAR FEATURES ONLY	PLAN B: ADD SPACE AND SOLAR FEATURES	PLAN C: REBUILD	DESIGN YOUR RETROFIT (OR HAVE IT DESIGNED)	FORGET IT! YOU DIDN'T WANT TO GO INTO DEBT ANYWAY!

GO IT ALONE BYPASS

LOAN REJECTED ROUTE

4.0 GET THE HELP YOU NEED TO COMPLETE YOUR RETROFIT	HAVE SOLAR DESIGNER REVIEW YOUR PLANS-SUGGEST IMPROVEMENTS	HAVE WORKING DRAWINGS (BLUEPRINTS) DONE	GET WRITTEN ESTIMATES OF LABOR AND MATERIALS COSTS	PRESENT DRAWINGS & ESTIMATES TO LENDING INSTI-TUTION OR AUNT HARRIET	SECURE A LOAN

BORROWER'S ROUTE

COWARD'S RETREAT

RICH FOLKS' ROUTE

5.0 BUILD THE RETROFIT (OR HAVE IT BUILT WHILE YOU WORK)	PURCHASE BUILDING MATERIALS	LINE UP CONTRACTOR & SUBS (IF USED)	SECURE BUILDING PERMIT	NOTICE: THIS IS YOUR LAST CHANCE TO BACK OUT AND GIVE BACK THE BORROWED MONEY

6.0 ENJOY THE RESULTS OF YOUR RETROFIT	LIVE IN IT OR WITH IT! GROW PLANTS OR FOOD IN IT	PAY LOWER FUEL BILLS	TAKE ADVANTAGE OF INCOME TAX CREDITS	... AND LIVE HAPPILY EVER AFTER

THE END OR THE BEGINNING

4-1. The Great Retrofit Steeplechase

FINDING A DESIGNER

The best way to locate a designer is to inquire among the people you know. You can also watch for feature articles in local newspapers that display the work of such individuals. Or, if you happen to pass a house in your area that appears to have passive solar features, knock on the door and ask who designed the house. This may seem a bit bold, but you will probably discover that the owners are eager to help. In addition, this is an excellent way to meet interesting people—or have doors slammed in your face.

If the direct approach does not appeal to you and you are not able to locate a designer by any other means, check your telephone directory. Unfortunately, the yellow pages has no category for passive solar designers. Most directories list only two categories under solar energy, "Solar Energy Equipment" and "Solar Energy Research & Development." Although neither category has anything to do with design work, you will probably find a designer or two listed under one or both of them. If not, cast about in the white pages for a listing like "Solstice Designs," "Sundance Designers," "Solar Design Group," "Sunspacers," "Daystar Design," "Solar Lifestylers," or whatever. The problem is that designers are usually as creative in naming their firms as they are in their work, so you may not find them listed as you think they should be.

CONSERVATION AND
RENEWABLE ENERGY
INQUIRY AND REFERRAL
SERVICE

P.O. BOX 1607
ROCKVILLE, MD 20850
800/523-2929
IN PENNSYLVANIA: 800/462-4983
IN ALASKA & HAWAII: 800/523-4700

4-2. Conservation and Renewable Energy Inquiry and Referral Service

When you have located several designers, discuss your plans with them and select the one you think will do the best job for you. Inquire about their previous work, the exact services they provide, and the cost of such services. As is true of any profession, the capabilities and experiences of people in the solar design area vary greatly from person to person. Find a designer who can calculate the performance potential of your retrofit either by hand calculations or computer simulations. Most importantly, find someone whose judgment you trust.

LOCATING AN ARCHITECT

If you prefer to work with a registered architect, try to find one who specializes in passive solar design. Keep in mind that not all architects are competent in this area. Again, ask around—see if anyone you know can recommend an architect—or try the telephone directory and start calling. When you find an architect who inspires your confidence, arrange an initial appointment to discuss your plans. The initial consultation should be free. After the discussion of services and fees, you should be able to decide what help you need and what help you can afford.

If you plan to have an architect do all of the design work, produce working drawings, and supervise the construction of your retrofit, these services will probably add 12 to 15 percent to the cost of your project. If you cannot afford all of these services, you may be able to employ the architect on an hourly basis to provide specific help along the way.

A good architect is both a technician and an artist who can help you translate your ideas into a reality and save you money by devising the most cost-effective and aesthetically appealing design solution. If you can afford the services of an architect, you will no doubt find that the expense is justified by the results.

If you decide to employ a solar design professional or an architect but have difficulty locating such a person, call the Conservation and Renewable Energy Inquiry and Referral Service (CAREIRS) toll free at (800) 523–2929;

from Pennsylvania (800) 462–4983; from Alaska or Hawaii (800) 537–4700. Along with much other valuable information, CAREIRS can provide you with a listing of solar designers in your area.

OTHER HELPFUL PEOPLE AND PROGRAMS

If you choose not to employ a designer or architect because of the expense involved, other less costly and even some no-cost alternatives are available for design help. A nearby college or university may have a faculty member or even a group of people who can offer you advice. Such a person or group would most likely be associated with the engineering, architecture, or environmental affairs departments. If there is a local or state chapter of the American Section of the International Solar Energy Society (AS/ISES) in your area—perhaps affiliated with a university—you will undoubtedly find that its members are both knowledgeable and helpful.

Some communities have organizations such as "solar action teams" that offer services on a local or regional basis. The people in these groups often work as volunteers and are usually quite experienced in retrofit work—especially the building of low-cost attached solar greenhouses and thermosiphoning air panels. A local community services directory should contain a listing for such a group in your area if it has one.

Another potentially valuable source of assistance with the planning, design, financing, and construction of your retrofit could be the utility company that supplies your electricity or natural gas, or in some cases, your supplier of home heating oil. Call the local office of the utility or oil supplier and ask if they are operating a Residential Conservation Service (RCS). If they offer this service, you should be able to arrange a home energy audit to evaluate the energy efficiency and solar potential of your home. This service will cost $15 or less, and it may even be free. The person who does the audit should be able to recommend needed in-

sulation and weatherization, as well as the type of passive solar retrofit that would be most effective for your home. This person should also be able to estimate the cost of the retrofit and the approximate annual energy savings resulting from it. In addition, you may want to inquire about loan programs and get recommendations for people who could construct the retrofit. Some utilities that have RCS programs also offer loans—sometimes at low-interest or no-interest rates—for passive solar retrofits to individuals who qualify.

PROFESSIONAL CONSULTING SERVICES

If you do not work with a professional designer or architect and you are planning a relatively major addition or revision of the structure of your house, it would be wise to have a structural engineer or experienced remodeling contractor review your plans. If the addition or revision will add considerable weight to the earth around your house, you may also want to have a soil engineer check the load-bearing capacity of the soil. Structural engineers, remodeling contractors, consulting architects, and soil engineers can usually be employed on an hourly basis for consultation. While not exactly what you would call cheap, the services of such professionals are relatively inexpensive in comparison to the cost of potential disasters they may help prevent.

DRAFTING SERVICES AND WORKING DRAWINGS

Whether you do the work on your house yourself or hire a contractor, it is a good idea to have a set of working drawings (blueprints) if you are doing a Plan B or C retrofit. You will probably have to present drawings to the lending institution if you are going to borrow money, and you will also need drawings to secure a building permit in most cases. Furthermore, working drawings help to ensure that the work on your house will be done correctly, and they can serve as the official documents if a question about whether some part of the work was designed or constructed properly ever arises. Construction drawings will almost certainly be necessary to get bids from contractors or subcontractors for the part of the project you want them to complete.

Architects or solar designers will usually provide working drawings as a part of their service. Be aware that such drawings do not always include all of the construction details they should have. Because many building-trades people are not familiar with some of the techniques used in passive solar applications, the details contained in the blueprints are very important to the success of the project. Make sure that the blueprints contain the details necessary to actually construct the features they represent. (The illustrations in chapter 5 should be helpful for this purpose.) At the same time, be aware that not every aspect of the project can be shown in detail and that some details must be worked out during the construction process.

You should also ask your designer or architect to make a building materials list specifying the exact varieties, quantities, and sizes of lumber needed, as well as sizes and manufacturers of other materials such as glazing, windows, and doors. Such a list will save you many hours of calculating, telephoning, and shopping around, and you will be able to use the list to get estimates of the cost of materials. If you employ a contractor, that person could also draw up the materials list.

If you do not employ a designer or architect, you can have your working drawings done by an architectural drafting service. Such service can be contracted on either an hourly or a flat rate basis. It is important to tell the draftsperson exactly what you want, since the job of this person is only to draw your plans, not redesign your house.

Finally, if you do not need to borrow any money for your retrofit; if a building permit is not required; if you are going to do most of the actual construction yourself; and if you already know, or can figure out as you go, exactly how everything should be built, you probably do not need working drawings. Working drawings will not be needed for some of the less complex retrofits, such as those described under Plan A in chapter 3. The construction details in chapter 5 should contain sufficient information to allow you to build most of the Plan A options without having additional drawings done.

DECIDING WHETHER TO HIRE A CONTRACTOR

A contractor's role in the construction process is to supervise a building project and line up subcontractors, such as framers, finish carpenters, masons, and electricians, to complete various jobs associated with the project. Although contractors are sometimes called builders, they may or may not do any of the actual construction work themselves. The contractor is responsible for ensuring that workers and materials are at the construction site when needed and that the project is completed according to the plans within a specified time and budget. A contractor's experience and connections in the local housing industry can save you a great deal of time and allow you to place the responsibility for your project in someone else's hands. Obviously, this costs money. Employing a contractor may add 15 to 20 percent to the cost of your project.

You can decide whether to hire a contractor on the basis of three criteria: your own skills, the amount of time, and the amount of money you have to spend on your retrofit project. The trade-offs are very simple: if you have the skills, interest, and time to serve as your own contractor, you will save money. If you are the contractor, however, you must be at home every day while the work is in process—at least long enough to get workers started in the morning and check their work at the end of the day. You can also expect to spend part of your day ordering materials and seeing that they are delivered on time and in good condition. Part of your evenings will be spent calling subcontractors who are not at home during the day to arrange for completion of the work needed to keep the project going. You will also need time for planning the next day's work. (This all adds up to what most people would consider a full-time job!)

In addition to saving money, serving as your own contractor has other advantages. By accepting the responsibility for project management, you will not have to spend energy deciding who is to blame and how you are going to sue him if something goes wrong. In all likelihood you understand what you are trying to do better than anyone else ever could. If you take charge of construction and workers are directly responsible to you, there is a better chance that the work will be done the way you think it should be done. It makes a great deal of sense to take charge of your own project—just as it does to take charge of your own life—since you are going to pay for and live in (or with) whatever you build. Most important, you will experience the satisfaction, and sometimes the frustration, that results from taking an active role in creating your own living environment.

SELECTING A CONTRACTOR

If you are doing a Plan B or C retrofit and you decide to employ a contractor, try to find one who specializes in solar remodeling work. In some parts of the country, firms or individuals will not only design but also construct your retrofit. If you can find such a company or person in your area, it would be worth your time to investigate their services.

Although a licensed contractor should be capable of building whatever you need, not all contractors are familiar with the techniques used in passive solar applications, such as installing insulation on the outside of a wall. Some of the work required for your retrofit will probably run against the grain of experience of many contractors. You should not have to spend your time hassling with a contractor who insists that you or your designer are wrong. ("After all, everyone knows insulation goes on the *inside*....") Be sure you find a contractor who has a good feel for what you want to do and knows how to accomplish it.

As always, the best way to locate a contractor is on the basis of recommendations from other people who have employed him or her. The Conservation and Renewable Energy Inquiry and Referral Service (CAREIRS) can also provide a list of contractors and subcontractors in your area who specialize in solar remodeling projects. If you cannot find a contractor through recommendations or CAREIRS, call a member of the local Bonded Remodelers Council and ask for a list of contractors in your area. You might also ask if any members of the council specialize in passive solar retrofits.

After you identify possible candidates, you should be able to decide on the basis of several discussions whether you would want a given person to serve as your contractor. You should not have to pay for these initial consultations. When you have narrowed down the field to two or three acceptable candidates and they have reviewed your plans, they should be able to draw up a materials list if you do not already have one. The contractors should then be able to give you a written estimate of the total cost of the project.

Many contractors and subcontractors will offer to work on a "time and materials" basis. (Translation: "I'll do the work for you, and we'll see how long it takes and how much it costs; then I'll tell you how much you owe me.") This is not a satisfactory approach, especially to lending institutions from which you may want to secure a loan. Also unsatisfactory are contractors who are unable to estimate precisely how much time will be required for a project and therefore estimate high to protect themselves. If they have overestimated, they are not likely to refund any money if the job takes less time or costs less than they had projected. This being the case, get written estimates from two or three contractors and award the contract to the person you want to do the work. (It would be best not to sign any agreement, however, until you have lined up your finances.) The actual dollar figure of a contractor's estimate should not be your only consideration. You should also give equal weight to the contractor's reputation and your sense of how well you and the contractor would work together.

SUBCONTRACTORS

If you employ a contractor, he or she should arrange for subcontracted labor and services needed to complete the project. You must do this yourself if you are the contractor. Subcontractors, or "subs" as they are often called, include framers (rough-in carpenters), finish (or trim) carpenters, cabinetmakers, masons, concrete workers, insulation and drywall installers, electricians, and plumbers.

If you will be hiring subcontractors, first decide what portion of your retrofit you are going to do yourself, then get estimates, and later, contract the remaining work to subs. Be aware that what you *can* do and what you *actually* do may differ. Perhaps the best illustration of this phenomenon is installing fiberglass insulation. Most people *can* do it, but when it comes down to it, few people want to.

You should be able to find the subs you need through personal recommendations, reading the doors of pickup trucks at construction sites, or listings in the yellow pages. Or you might call a contractor for recommendations. When you have identified people or firms who are able to do the work you need to have done and who can do the work when you need it done, you should get two or three estimates for each job. Select the subcontractors that you believe will do the best work in relation to cost. So that your project will not suffer unnecessary delays, you must prepare a work schedule (see chapter 5) based on how long each job will take; then schedule the subs accordingly. (Take this schedule with you if you are going to get a loan; it will make you appear as though you "have your act together.")

After you have made your financial arrangements and have secured a building permit, select the subs you want to employ and have them sign a contract specifying the cost of labor and materials and the time allotted for completion of the work. The contract should also specify who will purchase the materials, the sub or you. A contract form for subcontractors is included as Appendix C. Use it; it may save you some grief.

FINANCING YOUR RETROFIT

Several traditional alternatives are available for securing a loan to complete your retrofit. You could apply for a home improvement loan using the equity in your home as collateral or seek a personal loan using some other form of collateral. Personal loans are sometimes more difficult to arrange, however, and usually carry a higher interest rate. Two other possibilities, neither of which is recommended, are to remortgage your home and to seek a second mortgage.

You should think of your retrofit as an improvement to your home, particularly if it involves adding space. It makes the most sense, therefore, to apply for a home improvement loan if you are doing a Plan B or C retrofit. On the other hand, a personal loan might be preferable for smaller projects, such as those included under Plan A options.

FEDERAL INCOME TAX CREDITS*

The time to consider tax credits is while you are planning your retrofit, not after it is constructed. The regulations on solar tax credits

* Tax regulations referred to herein were current for the 1980 tax year. Since that time the IRS has been working on rules that could revise the eligibility of passive solar systems. Please check for subsequent changes in the tax laws.

specified in the August 29, 1980, issue of the *Federal Register* allow you to claim a credit of 40 percent of the cost of "materials and components whose sole purpose is to transmit or use solar radiation." Although a maximum of $4,000 is allowed for renewable energy devices, if the credit you are entitled to exceeds the tax you owe in a given year, it can be carried over to the next year. In order to claim the full $4,000 credit, $10,000 of the cost of your retrofit would have to qualify. Credits may be claimed for expenses incurred between April 19, 1977, and January 1, 1986, for solar applications to your principal residence. Credits can be claimed only when the work is completed or nearly completed as defined in the regulations. The solar devices must also have a useful life of at least five years.

If all of this sounds too good to be true, it is. The regulations in effect for the 1980 tax year ruled out credits for components of passive solar systems that serve a "dual function." What this means in a practical sense is that if, for example, you include a Trombe wall in your retrofit, the cost of building the wall itself would not qualify for a tax credit if the wall also supports the roof. It, therefore, has a function in addition to serving as thermal storage mass. Since the glazing on the Trombe wall, however, does not provide a view of the back yard, it is eligible for tax credit, since its sole function is to collect and trap solar energy. A Trombe wall that did not support the roof or other structural element *might* qualify, but a specific ruling by the Internal Revenue Service would probably be required in such a case.

In order to qualify for federal income tax credits, your retrofit must be properly designed and include the following five features in appropriate combination:

1. a solar collection area (south-facing glazing)
2. an absorber surface (dark-colored walls or floors in direct sunlight)
3. a storage mass (masonry, water, PCM, or a rock bed)
4. a heat distribution system (ducts, plenums, or fans)
5. a heat regulation system (vents, window insulation, sunshades)

The regulations state that "any shading, venting and heat distribution mechanisms or storage systems that do not have a dual function will qualify." By this definition thermal storage devices such as containers for water storage, waterwall tanks, and containers of phase change materials would probably qualify for tax credits, as would window insulation used to prevent heat loss or gain through south-facing glazing.

There is really only one foolproof method for determining what part of your retrofit will qualify for tax credits: get a ruling from the IRS. Such rulings are made on an individual basis, and the cumulative effects of these rulings help to define the interpretation of the regulations. To get a ruling on your retrofit, you will have to follow what the IRS calls "Revenue Procedure 80-20." It works like this: send a copy of your blueprints to the address below, along with a letter requesting review of the solar features of your retrofit. Enclose with these items a signed "perjury statement" (promising to tell the truth, the whole truth, and nothing but) and a "Section 61-10" statement, which gives the IRS the right to make public its ruling on your case, without using your name, of course. Copies of the 61-10 statement are available from the IRS. The review process may take three to six months, so file early if you want to get a ruling before you start building. Address your request for the appropriate forms and a ruling to: Internal Revenue Service, 1111 Constitution Avenue, N.W., Washington, DC 20224, Attn.: Dept. T:FP:T. A letter to the above address may get the process started and net you some helpful advice and a copy of "Revenue Procedure 80-20," but a definitive statement of what you can claim for tax credits can only be made by the procedure described above. Or you can always exercise your constitutional rights: read the regulations, make your own judgments, and let the chips fall as they may.

In addition to the credits allowed for renewable energy sources, you may receive a tax credit of 15 percent of the first $2,000 (for a total of $300) for expenses connected with energy conservation measures such as installing insulation, weather stripping, caulking, storm windows, storm doors, and other items such as automatic setback thermostats. These items are well defined in the regulations, so claiming credit for them is not difficult.

STATE INCOME TAX AND INCENTIVE PROGRAMS

At the time of this writing, most states have enacted legislation for either income tax credits or deductions, property tax exemptions, refunds, or other incentive programs designed to encourage the use of renewable energy sources.

These programs vary widely from state to state and range from 100-percent state income tax deductions for the cost of passive solar systems and exemptions from property tax for active-type solar collectors to sales tax refunds on equipment purchased. In states that have a state income tax, deductions or credits range from 0 to 100 percent. In most states that allow state tax credits for solar applications, such credits can be claimed *in addition* to federal tax credits. The chart in figure 4-3 prepared by the National Solar Heating and Cooling Information Center includes information on state tax credits, deductions, and exemptions. Check for recent changes in the incentive programs offered by your state.

4-3.

State Incentive Programs for Solar Applications

State	Property Tax Exemption	Income Tax Incentive	State Tax Exemption
Alabama	no	no	no
Alaska	no	up to $200 credit	not applicable
Arizona	exemption	up to $1,000 credit	exemption
Arkansas	no	100% deduction	no
California	no	up to $3,000 credit per application	no
Colorado	exemption	up to $3,000 credit	no
Connecticut	local option	no	exemption
Delaware	no	$200 credit for DHW systems	not applicable
District of Columbia	no	no	no
Florida	no	not applicable	not applicable
Georgia	local option	no	refund
Hawaii	exemption	10% credit	no
Idaho	no	100% deduction	no
Illinois	exemption	no	no
Indiana	exemption	up to $3,000 credit	no
Iowa	exemption	no	no
Kansas	exemption; refund based on efficiency of system	up to $1,500 credit	no
Kentucky	no	no	no

State	Property Tax Exemption	Income Tax Incentive	State Tax Exemption
Louisiana	exemption	no	no
Maine	exemption	up to $100 credit	refund
Maryland	exemption statewide plus credit at local option	no	no
Massachusetts	exemption	up to $1,000 credit	exemption
Michigan	exemption	up to $1,700 credit	exemption
Minnesota	exemption	up to $2,000 credit	no
Mississippi	no	no	exemption for colleges, junior colleges, and universities
Missouri	no	no	no
Montana	exemption	up to $125 credit	not applicable
Nebraska	no	no	refund
Nevada	limited exemption	not applicable	no
New Hampshire	local option	not applicable	not applicable
New Jersey	exemption	no	exemption
New Mexico	no	up to $1,000 credit	no
New York	exemption	no	no
N. Carolina	exemption	up to $1,000 credit	no
N. Dakota	exemption	5% credit for two years	no
Ohio	exemption	up to $1,000 credit	exemption
Oklahoma	no	up to $2,000 credit	no
Oregon	exemption	up to $1,000 credit	not applicable
Pennsylvania	no	no	no
Rhode Island	exemption	up to $1,000 credit	refund
S. Carolina	no	no	no
S. Dakota	exemption	not applicable	no
Tennessee	exemption	not applicable	no
Texas	exemption	not applicable	exemption
Utah	no	up to $1,000 credit	no
Vermont	local option	up to $1,000 credit	no
Virginia	local option	no	no
Washington	exemption	not applicable	no
W. Virginia	no	no	no
Wisconsin	exemption	no*	no
Wyoming	no	not applicable	no

Source: Prepared July, 1980, by the National Solar Heating and Cooling Information Center.

*Wisconsin offers a direct refund for part of solar expenditures; the refund is unrelated to taxes.

LOAN AND LOAN GUARANTEE PROGRAMS

In addition to the incentive programs already described, other federal, state, and locally administered loan and loan guarantee programs have been designed to encourage the use of solar energy for home heating and/or cooling.

HUD operates the "Section 312" property rehabilitation loan program, which provides direct loans at 3-percent interest to low- and moderate-income applicants who want to weatherize or solarize a one- to four-family residential structure that they own and occupy in a targeted urban area. If you and your project fit this description, check with the regional or area office of the Department of Housing and Urban Development, or write: HUD, 451 Seventh Avenue S.W., Washington, DC 20410.

The Federal Housing Administration's Home Improvement Loan Insurance Program will insure loans up to $15,000 for a period of up to fifteen years, at variable interest rates, for home improvements that include solar heating and/or cooling features. While no actual loans are made under this program, the fact of having this insurance sometimes makes your application look more attractive to a lending institution. Contact a HUD regional or area office, or write HUD in Washington for more information on this program.

The Veterans Administration's Energy Conservation Home Improvement Loan Program guarantees loans for conservation and solar energy improvements to existing homes owned and occupied by qualified veterans or their surviving spouses. If you already have a VA mortgage, you can probably qualify for this program. Check with your local VA office.

The Farmers Home Administration (FmHA) of the Department of Agriculture can make direct loans or issue interest credits to qualified applicants for the purpose of energy conservation and solar energy retrofits to existing homes in rural areas. If you are a resident of a town, village, or small city (population under 20,000) not associated with an urban area, you are eligible to apply for this program, if it is in operation in your area, whether or not you are a farmer. The program is operated through county or district offices of FmHA. If you have difficulty locating a local office, write: Farmers Home Administration, Department of Agriculture, Washington, DC 20250.

Another potential source of funding mentioned earlier, the Residential Conservation Service operated by utility companies, is certainly worth investigating.

Although the programs described above were in operation during the 1981 fiscal year, there is obviously no guarantee that they will still be in effect when you need a loan. When you are ready to investigate federal loan programs, check with the Conservation and Renewable Energy Inquiry and Referral Service. If it is still in operation—it is also supported by government funding—you can receive an updated listing of current incentive programs.

We can always hope that some insightful people in our government will continue to support programs designed to help people form their own personalized solutions to the energy crisis. Proposals have been made to spend billions, even trillions of tax dollars on such things as nuclear breeder reactors and solar-energy-transmitting earth satellites. You deserve some of that money for your own retrofit project. If for any reason none is available when you need it, be sure to express your thoughts to your elected representatives.

READY . . . SET . . .

After you have completed the planning, arranged your financing, and lined up the people who will help you with your retrofit project, the next step is to start building. The chapter that follows will help you get underway and guide you through the completion of your retrofit.

GO!

5.

Building It

To build anything, from a model airplane to an addition on your house, you must have certain skills, tools, and materials, and you need to know how it is supposed to be built. This chapter provides information to help you select materials and build various features of your retrofit. The information contained in this chapter cannot, however, give you the skills to run a crosscut saw, frame a wall, or lay concrete blocks, for example. These skills must be learned through experience. Failing that, you must hire someone or find a friend who does have the necessary skills and tools.

LEARNING THE SKILLS

In recent years a number of excellent owner-builder schools have opened across the country. Part III of Appendix D contains a list of some of these schools. Most of them specialize in training people with no previous building experience to build inexpensive, energy-efficient new homes or to retrofit existing homes. Ses-

sions usually last one or two weeks. This is certainly an interesting and productive way to spend a vacation, but you will incur expenses for travel, meals, lodging, and tuition. If this is not your idea of how to spend a vacation, you might enroll in an adult vocational training program offered in your area. Many school districts and community colleges offer classes related to the building trades. Such classes usually provide an excellent means for learning new skills in your spare time.

If you are not already a skilled do-it-yourselfer and do not have the time or interest to attend an owner-builder school or adult education classes, you are left with three basic options: (1) hire someone who has the skills to build what you need; (2) work as an apprentice to such a person so you can learn the skills; or (3) muddle through with the help of an experienced friend who has the skills. A combination of the first two options will have you working on your own house while you are learning the skills. The third option, muddling through, is used by thousands of people in all kinds of situations, usually with surprising results— be they surprisingly excellent or surprisingly disastrous.

BUYING MATERIALS

No matter who does the actual construction of your retrofit, you will ultimately be paying for the materials used. If you employ a contractor or subcontractors, these people may supply the necessary materials. In that case always insist on having a copy of the sales receipt for the materials they supply. This may become a problem if they purchase materials for other jobs at the same time or if they have arranged with the supplier to write a receipt for you with an amount higher than they actually paid for the materials. You may, therefore, find it more desirable to establish your own account with building material suppliers so that you can keep track of expenses for materials. Be sure to specify who may use the account if you plan to allow people who work for you to pick up materials for your project.

Many of the larger building supply firms have a sales representative who works with owner-builders. It is this person's responsibility to service such accounts and offer the best possible prices on large purchases of materials. Although you may be able to receive a 10- to 20-percent discount on a large order, a cash-and-carry dealer who caters to do-it-yourselfers may offer you better prices overall. Be sure to add the cost (and hassle) of transporting materials to your house, since cash-and-carry dealers do not provide delivery service. If you own a truck, you are home free, but if you have to rent one or pay someone to deliver the materials, you may be better off buying materials at a higher price if the delivery is included.

When purchasing building materials, shop around just as you would for any other major purchase. Give your materials list to three or four building supply firms and get an estimate on the total cost of the materials, including delivery from each. Give your business to the supplier who offers the best prices, the best services, and, most importantly, the best materials. The same materials, say 2- by 6-inch (5- × 15.2-cm) lumber, from two different dealers may vary greatly in quality.

You may be accustomed to handpicking your lumber from the stock available at the local lumberyard, then having it delivered the same day and stacked neatly where you want it. In most parts of the country, however, the days when this was possible are gone forever. You are more likely to find that with larger dealers you must place your order several days in advance; when they get around to filling it, they will probably take whatever you ordered from the top of the pile, load it in a truck with a forklift, drive to your house, and dump it wherever they please if you are not at home. This saves the supplier considerable time and hand labor, but sometimes results in your receiving unacceptable materials. For example, you may find that two out of ten 2- by 4-inch (5- × 10.2-cm) studs you ordered are badly twisted, warped, or crowned. It is advisable, therefore, to check each delivery when it arrives and send back any damaged or unacceptable material for replacement. If you let it be known that you will accept nothing that is substandard, you are less likely to receive such materials with subsequent deliveries.

SELECTING APPROPRIATE MATERIALS

The following recommendations should help you with the task of buying the proper materials for your project. Use these as guidelines when ordering materials.

Lumber

■ Use readily available standard sizes of lumber whenever possible.

■ Use construction-grade (#3) lumber if it will be covered with finish materials, as in studs in a wall.

■ Use #1- or #2-grade lumber where it will not be covered.

■ Use fir or yellow pine (or whatever is the strongest and least expensive wood in your area) for structural components such as floor joists. Do not use low-strength or lightweight woods such as cedar for structural components.

■ Use redwood, cypress, or cedar for trim that will be exposed to the elements or to moisture, either outdoors or in a sunspace, for example.

■ Use expensive wood (e.g., clear white pine, walnut, etc.) sparingly, and only when appearance or your personal wealth justify the added expense. (Do not use expensive wood if it is to be painted; this is an offense to nature's handiwork!)

■ Use the variety of lumber that is most readily available in your area as exterior siding or structural components; go to a local sawmill back in them there hills and see what you can buy. All of it will probably be rough-sawn—very rough.

Masonry Materials

■ Use 4- by 8- by 16-inch (10.2- × 20.3- × 40.6-cm) solid concrete "cap" blocks for building 8-inch- (20.3-cm) or 16-inch- (40.6-cm) thick thermal storage walls; or use hollow-core blocks and fill the cores with poured concrete or grout mix. (Do not use light aggregate block for thermal storage walls.)

■ Use rough-textured or corrugated-face blocks for thermal storage walls in direct sunlight. (These have more surface area than smooth-faced blocks.)

■ Use monolithic (poured) concrete walls for thermal storage walls if the cost of pouring the walls is less expensive in your area than the cost of the labor and materials needed to build the wall.

■ Use dense, dark-colored stone if you are going to use stone as the facing or structural material on thermal storage walls.

■ Use unglazed, dark-colored quarry tile, brick, or pavers to cover concrete floors. Dark-colored slate or flagstone can be used but will not retain the heat as well as brick or quarry tile. (Do not use glazed tile or glazed brick as a floor covering because reflection from the floor surface reduces the amount of heat that can be absorbed.)

■ Use 2- by 8- by 16-inch (5- × 20.3- × 40.6-cm) solid concrete "cap" blocks as an inexpensive floor covering for concrete slabs or well-supported wooden floors in direct sunlight. These can be laid in any pattern desired. The entire exposed surface of the blocks should be grouted to produce a smoother finish, and the blocks should be stained a dark color and sealed before the floor is used.

■ Use specially formulated concrete stain or paint to color concrete floors if you cannot afford to have them tiled or bricked.

Drywall ("Sheetrock"; "Gypboard")

■ Use $\frac{5}{8}$-inch (1.6-cm) fireproof sheetrock for large expanses of cathedral or vaulted ceilings, particularly if direct or reflected sunlight will strike the ceiling. Also use this material around chimneys, fireplaces, and wood-burning stoves.

■ Use multiple layers of sheetrock to cover interior walls if added mass is desired; that is, order two or three times as much drywall as you would need to cover the walls with one layer.

■ Use sheetrock to cover the interior surface of masonry walls if you do not want to have the wall plastered. The sheetrock must be applied directly to the wall with construction-grade adhesive and short concrete nails. (No air space should be left between the masonry and sheetrock.)

Insulation

■ Use standard sizes and thicknesses of fiberglass batts or blankets for walls and ceilings. Buy them when they are on sale. (Or go out and find some in their natural habitat: it is said that fiberglass batts live in wall caverns.)

■ Use batts for 8-foot-high (2.4-m) walls; use blankets for ceilings with long expanses. (Use a continuous 6 mil polyethylene film, placed on the inside of the rafters, for a vapor barrier with fiberglass insulation blankets.)

■ Use foil-faced rigid insulation board with a rating of R-10 or -11 for sheathing materials on exterior walls.

■ Use 2- or 3-inch (5- or 7.6-cm) expanded polystyrene (beadboard) to insulate footing and perimeter of floor slab; apply with construction adhesive.

■ Use a fiberglass (or other insulating material) "seam sealer" between concrete foundation and stud-frame wall.

General

■ Use materials that have surfaces and textures that harmonize with the existing part of your house if you are planning an addition or rebuilding project.

■ Use window and door units that match or are compatible with existing doors and windows in your house.

■ Use salvaged building materials, available at your local home-wrecker's warehouse, if you want to save money and/or create a special look.

SCHEDULING WORK

What counts most in terms of your retrofit is getting it finished as soon as possible so you can receive the benefit of lower fuel bills and additional living space and so you can clean up the mess left by the construction process and get back to normal living. If other people are going to work for you, it is very important to schedule their time effectively so they will not be tripping over each other or waiting around while you are paying them. Work must proceed in a sequence; if one subcontractor's work is not completed, another subcontractor may be delayed. If you are doing all of your own work, you will probably set your own pace

in relation to the time and money you have available.

If you employ a contractor, that person will be responsible for scheduling subcontractors. If you serve as your own contractor, begin scheduling work a month or more in advance. The home-building industry in colder areas of the country traditionally operates on a seasonal basis and slows down considerably from November through February. You may find that subcontractors are easier to schedule during the off-season and that you can get better prices because subcontractors are looking for work during the late fall and winter months. Check around and plan your building project accordingly.

After you have decided when to build and you have received subcontractors' estimates of amount of time and money required for their part of the work, you can begin to make a work schedule such as the one in figure 5-1. You will, of course, also need to consider how much of your own time will be available to supervise the project—whether or not you are the contractor.

Suppose that you are planning to build a $12,000 solar addition to your house and the only time you have available to supervise the project is July and August. If you wanted to complete the work within five or six weeks, your schedule might look something like the one in figure 5-1.

Including the approximate cost of materials and labor for each step of the work will help you determine your cash flow requirements. If you secure a home improvement loan, for example, you may be required to complete some portion of the work, or perhaps all of it, before you can receive the total amount of money you borrowed. Even if your lending institution will grant the full amount of the loan at one time, you might be able to work out a plan whereby you could draw money as you need it—say in four equal payments—allowing you to avoid paying interest on the money you borrow until you actually need to spend it. A schedule such as the one in figure 5-1 will also help you with this kind of financial planning.

| DATES | WORK TO BE COMPLETED | # DAYS | COST | |
			MATERIALS	LABOR
JULY 5-8	PREPARE FOUNDATION; DIG FOOTING, SET FORMS; POUR AND INSULATE FOOTING, FOUNDATION, AND FLOOR SLAB	4	$245	$600
JULY 12-16	FRAME IN AND ENCLOSE ADDITION; INSTALL SIDING AND ROOF DECKING	5	5,530	1,200
JULY 19	SHINGLE ROOF	1	448	95
20-21	INSTALL GLASS	2	715	600
22	ROUGH IN ELECTRIC	1	85	120
23	ROUGH IN PLUMBING	1	96	1,205
JULY 26	INSULATE WALLS & CEILING	1	250	200
27	INSTALL SHEETROCK	1	200	175
28-29	TAPE AND FINISH SHEETROCK HANG LIGHT FIXTURES	1	30	150
	INSTALL SWITCHPLATES, ETC.	½	—	60
30	SET PLUMBING FIXTURES	½	—	103
AUGUST 2-4	TRIM CARPENTRY	2	107	240
	PAINTING	1	54	80
9-11	INSTALL FLOOR TILE	3	605	1,250
			$8,405	$6,078
			$14,483.*	

* NOTE: THIS FIGURE REPRESENTS THE ACTUAL
COST OF A "$12,000" ADDITION

5-1. Work schedule—July–August, 1983

Although a schedule is necessary, you should not expect that the work on your project will proceed exactly as you have planned it—particularly if other people are involved. Some delays are inevitable and should be anticipated; leave a few days unscheduled to serve as catch-up time. The trick is to keep delays to a minimum. Murphy's Law ("If anything can go wrong . . .") may very well apply to your scheduling efforts, but you should recall that Murphy was an optimist.

WORKING WITH A CONTRACTOR OR SUBCONTRACTORS

How you relate to the contractor or subcontractors you hire will greatly affect the success of your project. The majority of contractors and subs are honest people trying to make a living through hard work. Most take pride in their work and do not appreciate working for people who treat them as servants. As is the case with all interpersonal relationships, you will probably find that these people will treat you, and their work for you, with about the same amount of respect as you treat them. Try to establish the fact that you expect their work to be of the same high quality it would be if they were building their own home. Communicate; talk to them; tell them what you are trying to accomplish and tell them exactly *what* you want them to do. Do not, however, make the mistake of telling them *how* to do their work. On the other hand, do not accept any work that is unsatisfactory, since you will have to live with any mistakes for a very long time. If you discover that something is unsatisfactory, although completed according to the plans, it will probably be worthwhile in the long run to have it changed—even if it costs you more money to have it corrected. Changing things as you go can become a very expensive hobby; the best way to avoid this is by good planning *before* you start building.

If you hire a contractor to manage your project, he or she is responsible for checking the quality of subcontractors' work. But, whether you have a contractor or not, the final responsibility for accepting the work still rests with you. The process works very simply: you pay for work only when it is completed to your satisfaction. Nonpayment should be used only as a last resort, however, and only after you have requested that the work in question be redone or repaired. Your close attention to the progress of the work will also do a great deal to avert possible confrontations that may arise from a lack of communication between you and the people you hire.

Should you get into legal battles with your contractor or subs over unsatisfactory work, keep in mind that in many states these people can place a contractor's lien against your property if they have performed work on your house for which you have not paid them. Once again, however, no such action needs to take place if you maintain open and honest communication with the people you hire.

Before you allow anyone, including your friends, to work on your house, check your insurance. Make sure you are covered or that workers provide their own coverage in the event of an accident. You might also want to consider having workers sign a waiver holding you blameless if they are injured through no fault of yours. Check with your lawyer.

It is very important that you spend your time and energy before and during the construction process thinking about what will go right rather than what could go wrong. Your own attitude toward what you are doing—which will be obvious to everyone involved—will probably have more to do with the success of your project than any other single factor.

Your attitude will undoubtedly be more positive if you have specific information about how the features of your retrofit should be built. The remainder of this chapter provides this kind of information in the form of outlines and illustrations. This information follows the "Plan A, B, and C" categories used in chapter 3 to describe the various retrofit options.

HOW IT'S SUPPOSED TO BE: PLAN A OPTIONS

ENLARGING SOUTH-FACING WINDOWS OR REPLACING A WINDOW WITH A SLIDING GLASS DOOR

1. Determine whether the south wall in which the unit is to be installed can be altered.
2. Determine whether the area of the wall to be altered has any plumbing or wiring in it.
3. Remove existing window unit; temporarily brace wall with jacks or sturdy lumber.
4. Remove portion of wall surfaces and insulation necessary to accommodate new unit.
5. Replace headers and cripple studs around existing window with headers and cripples that will span new window or door unit (see fig. 5-2).
6. Frame in opening to accommodate new window or door. (Inside dimensions of opening should be ¼ inch (.6 cm) larger on all sides than outside dimensions of new unit.)
7. Set new unit in opening; be sure that it is plumb and level; secure and fasten it in place; spray expanding-type single-element urethane foam in crack between unit and framing.
8. Insulate wall; apply interior and exterior wall finish and trim around new unit.

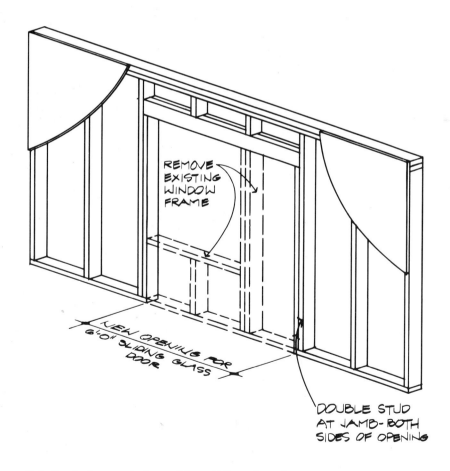

5-2. Replacing a window with a sliding glass door

ADDING A NEW WINDOW OR SLIDING GLASS DOOR

1. Determine whether the south wall in which the window or door is to be installed can be altered. (Check with a remodeling contractor or frame carpenter if you are uncertain.)
2. If the wall is of frame construction, find out where the studs are located. (Use a magnet to find the nails, tap on the wall, or look for the nails in exterior siding.)
3. Determine whether any plumbing or electrical wiring lies in the wall area where you want to place the window or door. If so, determine whether it can be rerouted.
4. Remove interior and exterior wall surfaces and insulation from area where unit is to be placed; brace wall with jacks or sturdy lumber.
5. Cut existing studs; build in header plates and cripples.
6. Frame in opening in wall to accommodate new window or door. (Inside dimensions of opening should be ¼ inch [.6 cm] larger on all sides than outside dimensions of new unit.)
7. Set new unit in opening (be sure it is plumb and level). Secure and fasten it in place; spray single-element urethane foam in crack between unit and framing.
8. Insulate wall; apply interior and exterior wall finish and trim around new unit.

ADDING MOVABLE INSULATION FOR WINDOWS AND SLIDING GLASS DOORS

1. Determine what type of movable insulation would be most feasible (see figs. 5-3, 5-4, and 5-5).
2. Purchase necessary materials.
3. Make (or purchase) insulating devices and install on windows or sliding glass doors.

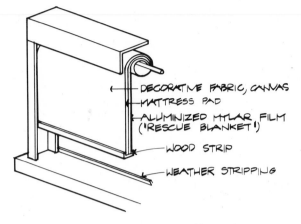

5-3. Insulating/reflective roll-down curtain

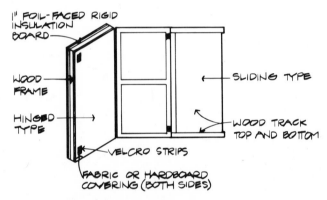

5-4. Movable window insulation

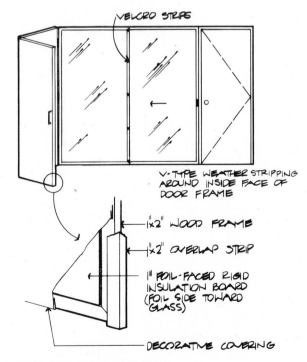

5-5. Bifold insulating shutters

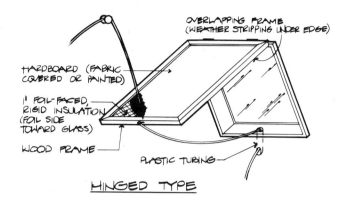

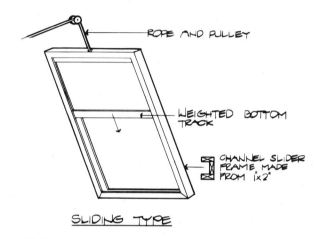

5-6. Skylight insulation

ADDING ROOF WINDOWS OR SKYLIGHTS

1. Examine the structural elements of the roof; determine where the rafters are and what size windows or skylights the south roof will accommodate with the least amount of alteration.
2. Remove interior covering and insulation (if any) from underside of roof.
3. Install headers between rafters to accommodate new unit(s); headers should be same size lumber as rafters; framing for new unit should be at least $\frac{1}{4}$ inch (.6 cm) larger on all sides than outside dimensions of unit.
4. Drive long nails through the roof, from inside, at the four corners of the opening so you can locate the exact area of roof decking and shingles to be removed from the exterior surface of the roof.

5. Remove exterior roofing material and decking from area where new unit is to be installed.
6. Set new unit in place and fasten to framing; spray expanding-type single-element urethane foam into crack between framing and new unit.
7. Install flashing and waterproofing material around new unit; replace roofing material as necessary to cover flashing.
8. Reinsulate roof around new unit; trim inside surface of unit.
9. Construct movable insulation shutters for new unit(s) (see fig. 5-5) or cut styrofoam panels, held in place with Velcro strips, over interior opening.

INSTALLING A SOLAR COLLECTOR WINDOW

1. Decide where to locate solar collector window on the south wall (unit can be installed in any existing window opening or a new opening can be cut: see above instructions for adding a new window or sliding glass door).
2. Install double-hung-type window as close to outside of wall surface as possible. (This unit should be double glazed, have a sill, and have an exterior finish that is weather resistant. Both the upper and lower sash should be operable.)
3. Install a standard-size (2-inch/5-cm) venetian blind (not a "mini-blind") behind double-hung window. (This blind should have a flat black or very dark upper convex surface and a gloss white, aluminum, or very light lower surface.)
4. Install a double-hung window as close to the interior wall surface as possible. (This unit should match the unit installed at the outside of the opening. It may be single glazed and should have removable sash to allow access for cleaning blinds and inside of exterior window. The interior and exterior windows should be 4 or 5 inches (10.2 or 12.7 cm) apart. Framing for interior window can be extended into the room if wall

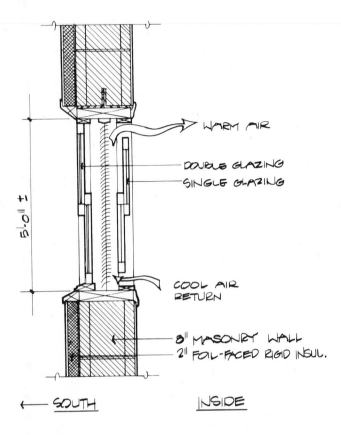

WARM AIR

DOUBLE GLAZING

SINGLE GLAZING

COOL AIR RETURN

8" MASONRY WALL
2" FOIL-FACED RIGID INSUL.

5'-0" ±

← SOUTH   INSIDE

5-7. Solar collector window (section)

thickness does not allow enough space between window units to hang venetian blind.)

Note: A solar collector window should not need night insulation if the window units are well sealed and venetian blinds are closed at night. Night insulation would, however, reduce heat loss from the window.

BUILDING A WINDOW BOX HEATER

1. Measure width of existing south window in which box heater is to be installed.
2. Determine angle of placement for box heater—perpendicular to the angle of the sun at noon on December 21 (see fig. 2-8). If the sun is 30° above the horizon at your

latitude at noon on December 21, the box heater should be slanted at about 60° from horizontal.
3. Determine appropriate length of box heater on the angle of tilt selected; allow space for a wooden prop under box so box will not rest on the ground.
4. Build wooden box of appropriate dimensions: the box should be 6 to 8 inches (15.2 to 20.3 cm) high, as wide as the opening in the lower sash of the window (minus $\frac{1}{4}$ inch/ .6 cm) and as long as it needs to be given the angle of tilt selected, minus adequate space to prop the box off the ground.
5. Insulate interior of box with 1-inch (2.5-cm) foil-faced rigid insulation board. (Foil side should face interior of the box.)
6. Install 1- by 2-inch (2.5- × 5-cm) frame midway between top and bottom edges of the box to hold absorber plate. (Frame should end 4 inches (10.2 cm) from the lower end of the box.)
7. Install absorber plate over frame. (Plate is also 4 inches/10.2 cm shorter than the box to allow for airflow between the air space under the plate and the air space above it.)
8. Install 1- by 2-inch (2.5- × 5-cm) glazing stop $\frac{3}{4}$ inches (1.9 cm) below top edge of box; apply butyl rubber bedding tape around top edge of stop.
9. Set glazing (safety glass, acrylic, or fiberglass) on stops; caulk around edges of glazing to form a watertight seal.
10. Install exterior glazing stop/trim.
11. Install box heater unit in window; place prop under it; weather-strip and seal space between heater and open window sash.

Note: Box heater should be removed or covered during months when no heat is required.

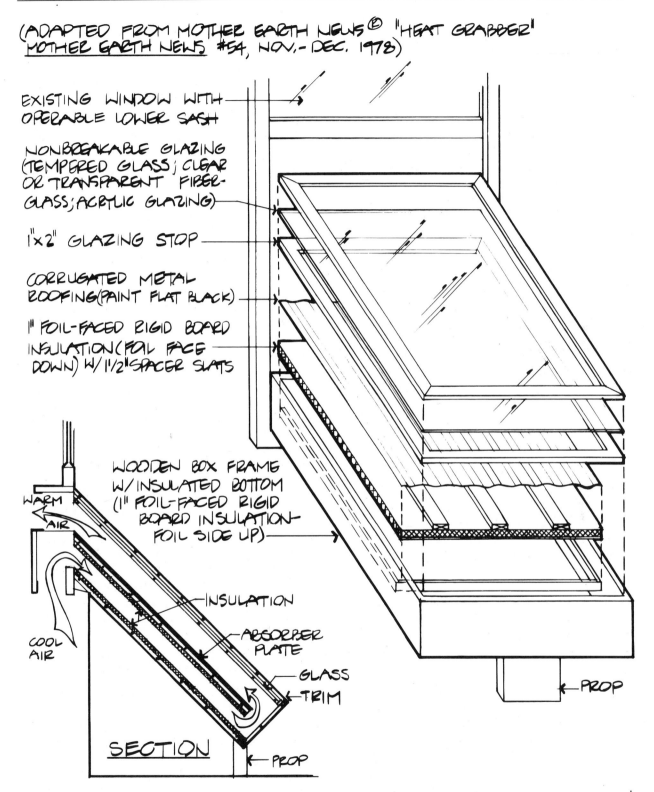

(ADAPTED FROM MOTHER EARTH NEWS® "HEAT GRABBER" MOTHER EARTH NEWS #54, NOV.-DEC. 1978)

EXISTING WINDOW WITH OPERABLE LOWER SASH

NONBREAKABLE GLAZING (TEMPERED GLASS; CLEAR OR TRANSPARENT FIBER-GLASS; ACRYLIC GLAZING)

1"×2" GLAZING STOP

CORRUGATED METAL ROOFING (PAINT FLAT BLACK)

1" FOIL-FACED RIGID BOARD INSULATION (FOIL FACE DOWN) W/ 1½" SPACER SLATS

WOODEN BOX FRAME W/ INSULATED BOTTOM (1" FOIL-FACED RIGID BOARD INSULATION-FOIL SIDE UP)

WARM AIR

COOL AIR

INSULATION

ABSORBER PLATE

GLASS

TRIM

PROP

PROP

SECTION

USED WITH PERMISSION OF THE MOTHER EARTH NEWS, P.O. BOX 70, HENDERSON, NC COMPLETE PLANS MAY BE PURCHASED FOR $10. FROM MOTHER EARTH NEWS   28791

5-8. Window box heater (exploded view)

CONSTRUCTING A THERMOSIPHONING AIR PANEL (TAP)

1. Locate an unobstructed area on the south wall of the house; select standard-size non-breakable glazing materials—34- by 90-inch (86.4- × 228.6-cm) or 34- by 78-inch (86.4- × 193-cm) patio door replacement units, for example. (If you select the glazing material first, you will know how much wall area will be required. On the other hand, if you determine how much wall surface is available, you will know what size glazing to purchase and how many TAPs you can install.)

2. When you have determined the size and number of TAPs you want to install, remove the siding from the wall in the area where TAPs are to be located. Cut 6- by 21-inch (15.2- × 53.3-cm) high and low vents through the wall.

3. Pour concrete foundation for TAP if you are not going to use braces under it; set foundation bolts while concrete is still pliable.

Note: The following instructions give details for constructing a TAP directly on a wall. You may find it easier to build the TAP separately and then installing it on the wall.

4. Build frame for TAP from 2- by 6-inch (5- × 15.2-cm) lumber; fasten frame to wall with mounting brackets; caulk around edge where TAP frame meets wall.

5. Apply 1 inch (2.5 cm) of R-11 foil-faced rigid insulation/sheathing board to wall area inside TAP frame with construction adhesive and square-head nails for styrofoam application. (Foil side of insulation board faces south.) Caulk around edges of insulation board and vents.

6. Install 2- by 2-inch (5- × 5-cm) absorber-plate stop frame to inside of 2- by 6-inch (5- × 15.2-cm) exterior frame of TAP.

7. Paint metal absorber plate (corrugated or raised-seam roofing material) with heat-re-sistant flat black paint; install plate over stops with roofing nails or rubber-gusseted nails.

8. Install 1- by 2-inch (2.5- × 5-cm) glazing stop to inside of TAP frame ¾ inches (1.9 cm) from front edge; apply butyl bedding tape to edge of stop that will meet glazing.

9. Install double-insulated tempered glazing (patio door replacement glass) or double-skinned acrylic in TAP; use rubber setting blocks under glass units; drill ⅛-inch (.31-cm) weep holes in structure under acrylic glazing to prevent condensation between layers.

10. Apply exterior 1- by 4-inch (2.5- × 10.2-cm) trim; use rough cedar or other wood covered with a good-quality paint.

11. Install back-draft damper in lower vent from inside house. (Flap on damper should open *into* TAP.)

Note: TAPs should be fully shaded during months when heat is not desired; if present roof overhang is not wide enough, it may be extended or a louvered overhang or roll-down sunshade may be installed.

CONSTRUCTING A RETROFITTED TROMBE WALL

1. Determine whether the wall to be used as a Trombe wall has any air spaces within it. If the wall is made of hollow-core concrete blocks, fill the cores with poured concrete with no gravel in it. (Access may be gained to the block cores by using a masonry hammer to break through the outside surface of the cores along the first hollow course of blocks below the bond beam blocks at the top of the wall. Concrete can then be "injected" into the cores through the holes at the top of the cores by using a large, home-made funnel made from sheet metal or composition roofing. Admittedly, this is a tedious process, but an unfilled hollow-core block wall will not work well.) If a double brick wall to be used in a Trombe wall has an air space between the two walls, it must

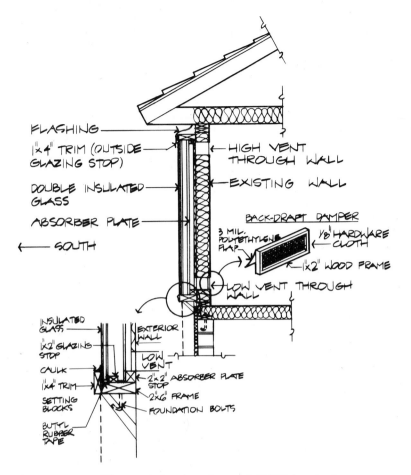

FLASHING

1"x4" TRIM (OUTSIDE GLAZING STOP)

DOUBLE INSULATED GLASS

ABSORBER PLATE

← SOUTH

HIGH VENT THROUGH WALL

EXISTING WALL

BACK-DRAFT DAMPER

3 MIL. POLYETHYLENE FLAP

1/8" HARDWARE CLOTH

1"x2" WOOD FRAME

LOW VENT THROUGH WALL

INSULATED GLASS

EXTERIOR WALL

1"x2" GLAZING STOP

LOW VENT

CAULK

1"x4" TRIM

2"x2" ABSORBER PLATE STOP

2"x6" FRAME

SETTING BLOCKS

FOUNDATION BOLTS

BUTYL RUBBER TAPE

5-9. Thermosiphoning air panel (TAP) (section)

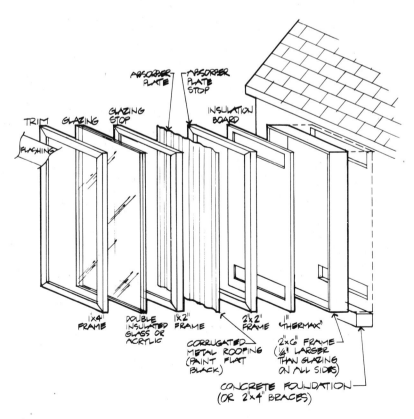

ABSORBER PLATE

ABSORBER PLATE STOP

INSULATION BOARD

TRIM GLAZING GLAZING STOP

FLASHING

1"x4" FRAME

DOUBLE INSULATED GLASS OR ACRYLIC

1"x2" FRAME

2"x2" FRAME

1" "THERMAX"

CORRUGATED METAL ROOFING (PAINT FLAT BLACK)

2"x6" FRAME (1/4" LARGER THAN GLAZING ON ALL SIDES)

CONCRETE FOUNDATION (OR 2"x4" BRACES)

5-10. Components of a thermosiphoning air panel (TAP)

be filled. To do this, first remove individual bricks every foot or so along the top of the outside wall, then inject concrete into the air space between the walls through the openings from which the bricks were removed. Finally, replace and remortar the bricks. (Do *not* fill the air space in a double brick wall unless you are reasonably sure both walls are structurally sound. If you are uncertain, have a mason check the wall.)

2. Determine how much of the south wall surface area you want to use as a Trombe wall (selecting the size and type of glazing first will help you determine how much of the wall surface you can cover with a given number of glazing units).

3. Decide whether to build a vented or unvented Trombe wall (see discussion in chapter 3). (Existing windows in wall could serve as high vents if the top of the windows open. Basement windows can serve as low vents if there is an air passage or register between the first floor and the basement along the north wall of the house. Similarly, the bottom of first-floor windows and the top of second-story windows in a two-story Trombe wall can serve as high and low vents if there is adequate airflow between floors. High vents in a Trombe wall should total ½ percent of the wall surface area; the area of low vents should also total ½ percent of the surface area of the Trombe wall.)

4. Remove any insulation from the interior or exterior of the wall section to be used as a Trombe wall.

5. Paint outside of wall with heat-resistant flat black paint or stain; allow to dry thoroughly before placing glazing over wall, or apply selective surface to outside of wall.

6. Pour a concrete foundation for Trombe wall glazing system to rest on; set foundation bolts in concrete while it is still pliable; insulate foundation down to the frost line with 2-inch (5-cm) expanded polystyrene beadboard.

7. Build framing system for glazing (see details, fig. 5-12); paint frame with heat-resistant white paint; allow to dry: attach frame to foundation bolts (use sill sealer

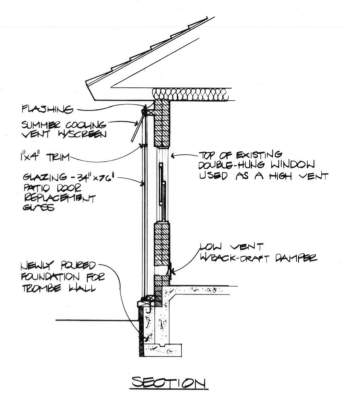

5-11. Retrofit Trombe wall (section)

between bottom of framing system and concrete foundation); bolt framing system to wall with lag bolts; use pipe spacers to hold framing away from wall to allow for airflow behind framing.

8. Apply butyl rubber bedding tape to surfaces that glazing will touch; place setting blocks on surface that glazing will rest on.

9. Thoroughly clean and install glazing; caulk and seal around glazing units with heat-resistant caulking to prevent air or water leakage.

10. Install back-draft dampers if low vents were cut through wall; dampers open *into* the Trombe wall. (If windows serve as vents, no dampers are required, since the windows, when closed, will prevent back drafts.)

11. Consider using a reflective surface such as anodized aluminum on the ground below the Trombe wall or arrange to have it snow when you need the most heat. (A reflective surface below the wall can potentially increase the heat-producing efficiency of the wall by as much as 40 to 50 percent.)

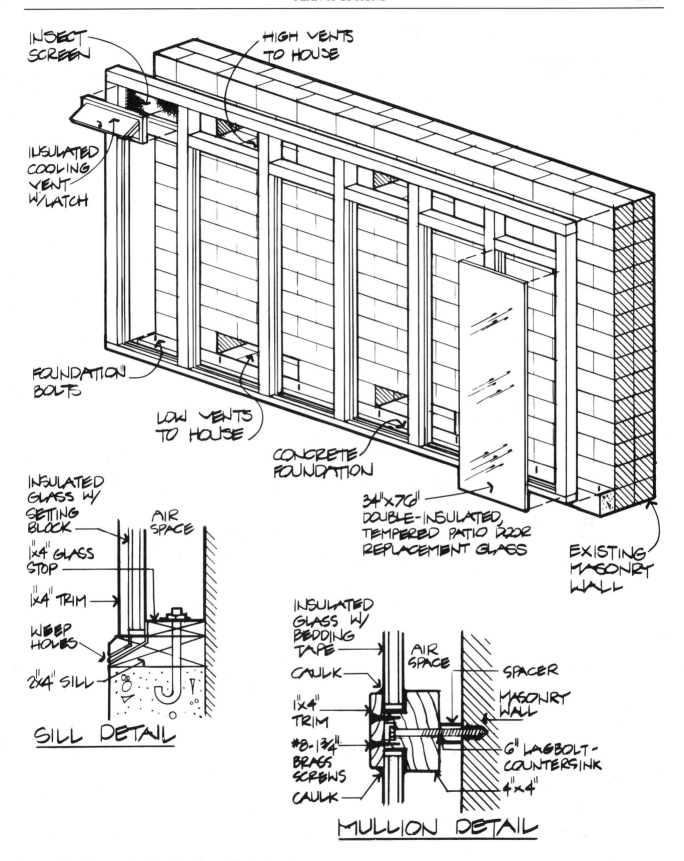

INSECT SCREEN

HIGH VENTS TO HOUSE

INSULATED COOLING VENT W/LATCH

FOUNDATION BOLTS

LOW VENTS TO HOUSE

CONCRETE FOUNDATION

34"x76" DOUBLE-INSULATED, TEMPERED PATIO DOOR REPLACEMENT GLASS

EXISTING MASONRY WALL

INSULATED GLASS W/ SETTING BLOCK

AIR SPACE

1"x4" GLASS STOP

1"x4" TRIM

WEEP HOLES

2"x4" SILL

SILL DETAIL

INSULATED GLASS W/ BEDDING TAPE

CAULK

1"x4" TRIM

#8-1¾" BRASS SCREWS

CAULK

AIR SPACE

SPACER

MASONRY WALL

6" LAGBOLT- COUNTERSINK

4"x4"

MULLION DETAIL

5-12. Framing section for Trombe wall glazing

Note: Trombe walls should be shaded during the months when heat is not required. A little sun on the wall will help create a beneficial stack effect in the air space between the glass and the wall, thus exhausting hot air through the exterior vents at the top of the Trombe wall glazing.

Glazing, paint, and caulking materials used in a Trombe wall should be able to withstand temperatures up to 200°F (93.3°C) without being damaged.

BUILDING AN INTEGRAL WATERWALL IN A STUD-FRAME WALL

1. Determine whether the foundation under your south wall could support the additional weight of a waterwall. (If the wall rests on a poured concrete or concrete block foundation wall on a footing that is in good condition, it could support the additional weight *if* the soil around your house has adequate load-bearing capacity. Check with a soil engineer if you are uncertain.)

2. Determine how much of the south wall you want to convert to a waterwall. (Existing windows can be removed to increase the size of the waterwall if there are enough windows remaining in the south wall to provide adequate ventilation and daylight to rooms adjacent to the waterwall.)

3. Determine the width between wall studs, center to center; the size of lumber used as studs in the south wall; and the presence of any plumbing or electrical wiring. If plumbing or wiring is in the way, see if it can be rerouted.

4. Contact manufacturers of modular waterwall containers to determine whether they manufacture tanks that would fit the existing spaces between the studs in your south wall. (Contact manufacturers months before you are ready to build your waterwall. Order the number and size of tanks you need; con-

sider buying tanks with a selective surface or tanks containing phase change materials.)

5. When the tanks arrive at your doorstep (not before) and you are absolutely certain they will fit in your wall, remove the siding, sheathing, and insulation from the exterior wall surface. If the interior wall is covered with sheetrock (drywall) or plaster, it can be left on *if* the water tanks are approximately the same depth as the studs. (If the tanks are thicker than the studs, the water tanks may protrude slightly inside or outside the studs and/or the studs may be furred-out—extended by nailing strips of the appropriate thickness to the edge of existing studs.) If the interior wall is covered with a material other than sheetrock or plaster—say, wood paneling—this material must be removed because it will insulate the water tanks from the living space.

6. Follow manufacturer's suggestions for venting the waterwall to the interior. Some manufacturers recommend a 4- to 6-inch (10.2- to 15.2-cm) continuous upper and lower vent running the entire length of the interior wall surface. Other manufacturers recommend that no vents be used because their tanks give off heat by radiation as does an unvented Trombe wall.

7. Build a framing system for the glazing like the one used for a Trombe wall (see fig. 5-12). (If cooling vents to exterior are used in the glazing system, both upper and lower vents would be required in the glazing system if there are no low vents between the waterwall and the house.)

8. Paint containers flat black *or* apply selective surface.

9. Paint glazing frame with highly reflective, heat-resistant white paint and attach frame to wall.

10. Thoroughly clean and install glazing units; caulk and seal around glazing with heat-resistant caulking to prevent air and water leakage.

11. Consider using a reflective surface below glazing (on ground) or a fold-down insulating/reflector shutter hinged at bottom and covered with material such as anodized

aluminum or mylar, to increase efficiency of the waterwall. (Fold-down shutter should fold five degrees below horizontal plane.)

Note: Waterwalls—especially those without vents—should be fully shaded during the months when no heating is needed.

BUILDING A FREESTANDING WATERWALL

1. (Follow step 1 from previous section.)
2. (Follow step 2 from previous section.)
3. Select and order the type of thermal mass storage containers to be used. (See information on sizing thermal storage mass in Appendix B; also see Appendix D for manufacturers of water and PCM storage containers.) Freestanding fiberglass water columns, culvert pipes, 55-gallon oil drums, PCM rods, pods, cans, or other containers such as 5-gallon oil cans or even half-gallon polyvinyl chloride milk containers can be used if they are tightly sealed and securely fastened in place.
4. Calculate the weight of containers when filled and be certain that the floor where they are to be placed can adequately support the added weight (1 gallon = 8 pounds; 1 l = .8 kg).
5. Determine what portion of your south wall could be removed and replaced with a load-bearing beam; that is, what portion of the wall could be opened up.
6. Open south wall and build framing system for glazing (see fig. 5-12). Both upper and lower exterior vents should be included in the framing system. Wood-frame awning windows or basement-type utility windows can be used as vents. Framing systems for glazing should be built into south wall, under load-bearing beams, to add back support to the wall.
7. Apply butyl rubber bedding tape to surface of inside stops that meet glazing; place setting blocks under glazing if patio door re-

placement units are used. Thoroughly clean and install glazing; caulk and seal around edges of glazing to prevent air and water leakage.

8. Place containers where they will receive direct sunlight from 9:00 A.M. to 3:00 P.M. during the heating season; anchor to floor and/or ceiling. Seal bottom of containers; fill with water; add a cup of liquid bleach and cover top surface of water with a slick of cooking oil to retard deterioration of water; seal tops of containers and finish building support system. (The support system must be able to prevent the containers from toppling in the event of seismic activity.)
9. Make or purchase roll-down insulating/reflective curtain (see fig. 5-3 and Appendix D) or other insulating system to cover glass at night, during cloudy periods in winter, and during the daytime in summer.
10. Consider using reflective surface on ground below glazing or a fold-down insulating/reflective shutter hinged at bottom and covered with anodized aluminum to increase the efficiency of the waterwall. (Shutter should fold down five degrees below horizontal.)

HOW IT COULD BE: PLAN B OPTIONS

ATTACHED SOLAR GREENHOUSE

1. Decide where greenhouse will attach to south wall and what its dimensions will be.
2. Select size and type of glazing material to be used—patio door glass, fiberglass glazing, double-skinned acrylic, or other glazing.
3. Decide upon the type of thermal storage mass to be used—water-filled oil drums, PCM storage rods, masonry walls, or concrete floors. (If partywall between greenhouse and house is an insulated masonry wall and radiant heat through the wall is desired, remove the insulation from the wall.)
4. Select the size and type of vents, operable windows, and doors to be used between house and greenhouse and between greenhouse and outdoors.

5. Install windows, sliding glass doors, or vents between house and greenhouse if existing openings are not adequate to handle airflow. (Upper vents to the house should total 9 to 10 percent of greenhouse floor area; lower vents should total 5 to 6 percent of greenhouse floor area.)
6. Plan and install water and electrical outlets in greenhouse.
7. Dig 18-inch-wide (45.7-cm) trench for footing of greenhouse foundation wall; footing should be poured a minimum of 12 inches (30.5 cm) below the frost line. Place 2-inch (5-cm) expanded polystyrene beadboard (styrofoam) along southernmost surface of the trench. Lay two reinforcing bars (re-bar) horizontally along the entire length of the bottom of the footing trench; these should be elevated about 4 inches (10.2 cm) above the bottom of the trench by placing rocks under them every few feet (.3 m). (Re-bar can also be dropped into concrete while it is still pliable.) Pour concrete into footing trench and set vertical re-bar or metal dowels every 4 feet (1.2 m) in footing when con-

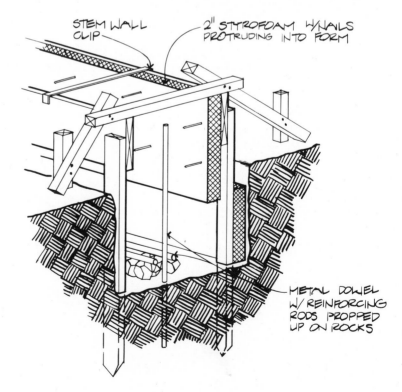

5-13. Forms for pouring integrated footing and foundation wall

STEM WALL CLIP

2" STYROFOAM W/NAILS PROTRUDING INTO FORM

METAL DOWEL W/ REINFORCING RODS PROPPED UP ON ROCKS

crete has cured sufficiently to support them; these should extend to a height of 2 inches (5 cm) below the height of the foundation wall.

Options:

a. If foundation wall (above footing) is to be of poured concrete also, pour the footing and foundation wall at the same time. (Use a form like the one in fig. 5-13.) Two-inch (5-cm) styrofoam beadboard should be placed on the inside surface of the southernmost form so that the styrofoam will adhere to the concrete as it cures; drive square-head nails (styrofoam nails) through the styrofoam before it is placed inside the form so that the nails protrude into the form. Place metal dowels vertically in center of opening between walls of form before concrete is poured. Set foundation bolts every 18 inches (45.7 cm) along top surface of concrete after it has cured sufficiently.

b. If foundation wall is to be constructed of solid or filled concrete block, the first block course is laid directly on the footing.

c. If louvered vents or operable awning-type windows are to be placed into the foundation wall, frames for the vents can be made of 2-inch-thick (5-cm) lumber treated with a wood preservative that is nontoxic to plants, such as zinc or copper naphthenate. These frames can then be suspended in the forms at the appropriate location with double-headed nails.

After the foundation is poured and the concrete sets, these frames will automatically be bonded into the foundation wall. (Vents or windows in a concrete block foundation wall can be integrated into block courses as the wall is built.)

d. Rigid insulation board, such as 2-inch (5-cm) styrofoam beadboard, can be sus-pended in the foundation wall forms rather than placed along the inside surface of the southernmost form wall as described above. This approach obviates the need for an external finish on the foundation wall. If this technique is used, the foundation wall should be 10 inches (25.4 cm) thick and the insulation board should be suspended with long nails about 3 inches (7.6 cm) inside the south surface of the foundation wall. (Insulation designed to be included in the pour is commercially available; see Appendix D.)

8. After foundation wall is completed, decide what area of the floor of the greenhouse, if any, will have a poured concrete floor; set forms and pour floor.

9. Place sill sealer (fiberglass or other type insulation strips) along top of foundation wall. Drill holes in sill plate to fit over bolts protruding from foundation wall. (The wooden sill plate should be 2 inches [5 cm] thick and as wide as the foundation wall.) Treat all surfaces of the sill plate with copper or zinc naphthenate wood preservative; bolt sill plate in place.

10. Frame in walls, mullions, and roof of greenhouse; treat wood with preservative.

11. Install insulation in solid portion of greenhouse roof. Install roof vent boxes or power roof vents, if used. Cover interior surface of solid roof with water-resistant sheetrock.

12. Fill planting beds with specially prepared soil mixture *before* greenhouse is enclosed. (It is much easier to fill the beds before the greenhouse is enclosed.) Cover soil with dropcloth to keep it clean during remainder of construction.

13. Build interior glazing stops, treat with wood preservative; allow to dry. Apply bedding tape to surface of stops that glazing rests on (place setting blocks under patio door replacement units, if used as glazing). Install glazing and caulk around it to prevent air and water leakage; apply and caulk around exterior stops (trim).

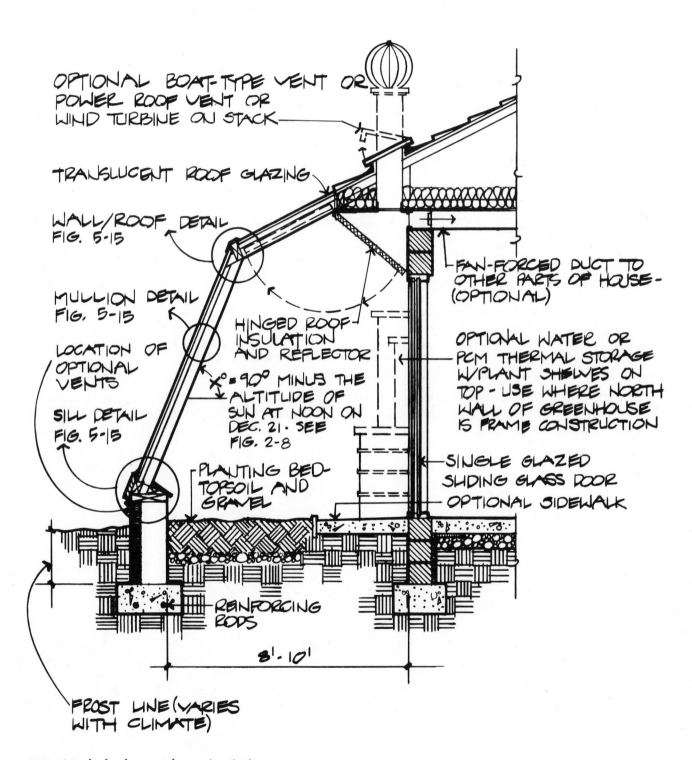

OPTIONAL BOAT-TYPE VENT OR
POWER ROOF VENT OR
WIND TURBINE ON STACK

TRANSLUCENT ROOF GLAZING

WALL/ROOF DETAIL
FIG. 5-15

MULLION DETAIL
FIG. 5-15

LOCATION OF
OPTIONAL
VENTS

SILL DETAIL
FIG. 5-15

HINGED ROOF
INSULATION
AND REFLECTOR

X° = 90° MINUS THE
ALTITUDE OF
SUN AT NOON ON
DEC. 21. SEE
FIG. 2-8

PLANTING BED-
TOPSOIL AND
GRAVEL

FAN-FORCED DUCT TO
OTHER PARTS OF HOUSE-
(OPTIONAL)

OPTIONAL WATER OR
PCM THERMAL STORAGE
W/PLANT SHELVES ON
TOP - USE WHERE NORTH
WALL OF GREENHOUSE
IS FRAME CONSTRUCTION

SINGLE GLAZED
SLIDING GLASS DOOR
OPTIONAL SIDEWALK

REINFORCING
RODS

8'-10'

FROST LINE (VARIES
WITH CLIMATE)

5-14. Attached solar greenhouse (section)

5-15. Attached solar greenhouse (details)

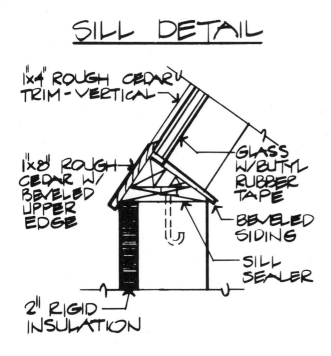

SILL DETAIL

1"x4" ROUGH CEDAR TRIM - VERTICAL

1"x8" ROUGH CEDAR W/ BEVELED UPPER EDGE

GLASS W/BUTYL RUBBER TAPE

BEVELED SIDING

SILL SEALER

2" RIGID INSULATION

MULLION DETAILS
1"x4" CEDAR — — CAULK

A.

BEDDING TAPE BOTH SIDES OF GLASS

CAP

GLAZING

BEVELED SIDING

OR

B.

CAULK — — 1"x4" CAP

1"x4" BATTEN

BEDDING TAPE BOTH SIDES OF GLASS

GLAZING

2"x8"

Note: If double-insulated glass, such as patio door replacement glass, is installed on an inclined angle, it is very important to construct the lower glazing stops on which the units rest in such a way that the stops will support both panes of the double-glazed unit equally. If more stress is placed on one pane, the seal on the unit could break, resulting in condensation between the two panes of glass.

14. Install windows, vents, and exterior doors for summer cooling. The combined total area of high and low vents should total 15 percent of the floor area of the greenhouse. The total area of low (inlet) vents should be less than the total area of high (outlet), and the vertical distance between high and low vents should be as great as possible.
15. Seal, caulk, and weather-strip entire greenhouse to create an airtight and bugproof environment.
16. Make (or buy) and install insulating/reflective curtains for greenhouse glazing.

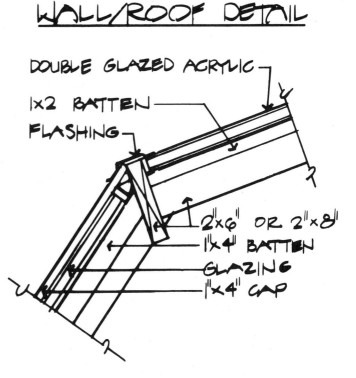

WALL/ROOF DETAIL

DOUBLE GLAZED ACRYLIC

1"x2" BATTEN

FLASHING

2"x6" OR 2"x8"

1"x4" BATTEN

GLAZING

1"x4" CAP

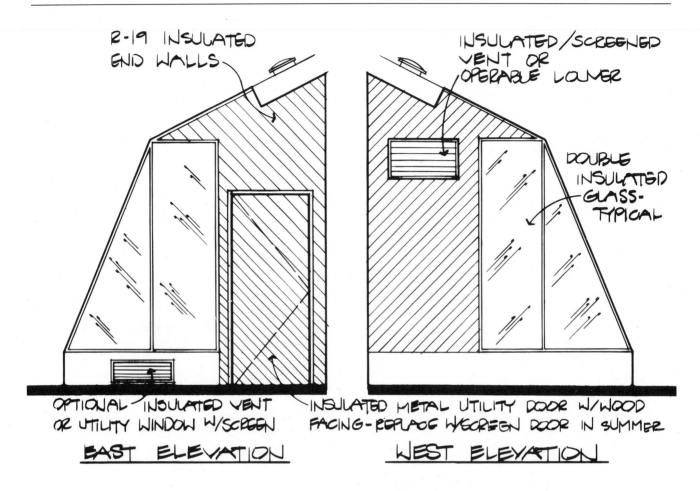

R-19 INSULATED END WALLS

INSULATED/SCREENED VENT OR OPERABLE LOUVER

DOUBLE INSULATED GLASS-TYPICAL

OPTIONAL INSULATED VENT OR UTILITY WINDOW W/SCREEN

INSULATED METAL UTILITY DOOR W/WOOD FACING-REPLACE W/SCREEN DOOR IN SUMMER

EAST ELEVATION

WEST ELEVATION

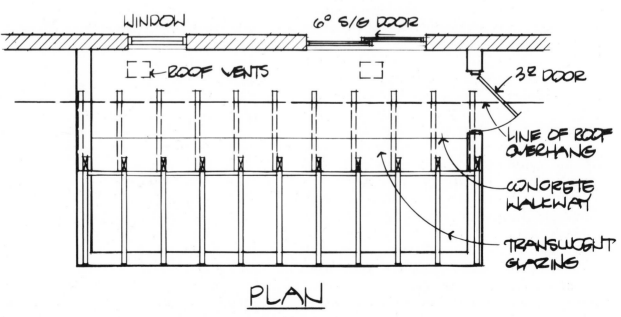

WINDOW

6° S/G DOOR

ROOF VENTS

3² DOOR

LINE OF ROOF OVERHANG

CONCRETE WALKWAY

TRANSLUCENT GLAZING

PLAN

5-16. Attached solar greenhouse (east and west elevations and plan view)

SUNSPACES

Because the design of sunspaces varies greatly, details for every variation cannot be provided. In general, the construction techniques and details used for an attached solar greenhouse may be adapted for construction of a sunspace. One or more of the following deviations from the details specified for greenhouses may be used to construct a sunspace.

1. Where possible, integrate sunspace into structure of the house (rather than attach it to the south wall) so that the north, east, and west walls of the sunspace adjoin living spaces. (If you have a U-shaped or L-shaped house, the sunspace could perhaps enclose the open portion of the U or L. Another approach would be to build interior masonry walls for the sunspace *inside* the house, then glaze the roof and south wall.)
2. Install glazing vertically (ninety degrees), rather than at a sloped angle, if you desire.
3. Do not glaze east and west walls; use at least R-19-insulated stud-frame end walls or masonry end walls insulated with 3 to 4 inches (7.6 to 10.2 cm) of styrofoam beadboard on the *outside*; paint beadboard or cover with a mesh and stucco system such as Dryvit (see Appendix D).
4. Do not glaze roof; continue slope of present roof to south wall of sunspace; use operable roof windows or skylights in sunspace roof.
5. Dig the floor of the sunspace into the ground a few feet (about 1 m) below the first floor of the house; expose the foundation (or basement) of the house to the sun.
6. Trim interior of sunspace with redwood, cedar, or cypress.
7. Incorporate an air lock entry to the house through the sunspace.
8. Use a hot tub or spa as a thermal storage (and people) container, but be sure to use a wood-fired or solar hot water heater to heat the water for the tub or spa. (Nice try, but a tub or spa is *not* eligible for income tax credits, although it will store heat and reduce temperature fluctuation in a sunspace.)
9. Incorporate thermal storage mass, such as water in containers, under counter-height worktables, benches, a bar, or a plant shelf along the north wall of the sunspace.
10. Duct excess hot air from the sunspace to the other portions of the house or to a rock storage bin under the house—in a crawl space, for example. Use low-volume fans in ducts.

SOLAR PORCH (SOUTH-FACING PORCHES ONLY)

1. Measure perimeter of porch; plan size of door opening, including framing, and low vent windows to exterior. Also, plan vent openings between porch and house.
2. Decide upon size and type of double glazing to use, such as patio door replacement units. Use double-skinned acrylic if privacy is desired. Determine placement of mullions to hold glazing (e.g., 3-foot [.91-m] centers to accommodate 34- by 76-inch [86.4- × 193-cm] patio door glass); incorporate existing pillars or supports where possible. A section of the northernmost portions of the east and west sides of the porch (next to the south wall of the house) could be enclosed and insulated to make up any leftover space on the east and west sides of the porch if the size of glazing selected does not work out exactly.
3. Insulate roof (ceiling) of porch to at least R-19. Remove ceiling covering, install insulation, and replace. Consider installing power roof vent or operable skylights in porch roof for summer ventilation.
4. Insulate perimeter of masonry porch floor and foundation with at least 2 inches (5 cm) of styrofoam beadboard held in place with construction adhesive. If porch has a wooden floor in poor condition, consider replacing it with a poured concrete floor. If the wooden floor is in good condition, add support under it by, for example, installing additional joists and cover the floor with 2- by 8- by 16-inch (5- × 20.3- × 40.6-cm) solid concrete "cap" blocks, laid in any brick floor pattern desired—two-by-two, herringbone,

etc. Cap blocks can be set in mastic or "thin-set" with no mortar joints between them. The surface of the blocks is then covered with a dark-colored grout mix and sealed.

5. Build 4- by 4-inch (10.2- × 10.2-cm) glazing support system (see fig. 5-12) with interior glazing stops. Install bedding tape on surface of interior stop on which the glazing rests.

6. Install glazing (use setting blocks under patio door glass); caulk around glazing.

7. Install exterior stops (trim); caulk around edges to prevent water and air leaks.

8. Make (or buy) insulating/reflective curtains or roll-down shades to control heat gain and loss.

SOLAR ADDITIONS

General guidelines and suggested construction details that could be used in a passive solar addition are included in this section. Since the details of any given passive solar addition vary, the suggestions provided below must be adapted to the specific addition you are building.

Foundation and Footing

■ Insulate and waterproof footing and foundation wall on the outside down to the footing—12 inches (30.5 cm) below the frost line.

■ Place anchor bolts (J bolts) into the foundation wall while concrete is still pliable if a stud-frame wall is to be built on foundation. Use an insulated sill sealer between foundation wall and frame wall. Also consider using a termite shield on top of the foundation, under the sill of the stud-frame wall.

Floor Slab

■ Treat soil under slab for termite protection; cover soil with at least 4 inches (10.2 cm) of compacted gravel or sand under floor slab; cover with a 6-mil polyethylene film for vapor barrier; pour 4-inch (10.2-cm) slab on top of vapor barrier. Do *not* insulate under floor slab if the floor is to be used for thermal storage and will not be covered with wood, carpet, or other floor covering with insulative qualities.

Masonry Walls

■ If wall is to be used for thermal storage in a direct gain situation, such as the interior north wall of an addition, or in an isolated gain situation, such as a partywall between an addition and sunspace, construct the wall of filled 8-inch (20.3-cm) concrete block with a rough texture or corrugated surface facing the sun.

Or use 4- by 8- by 16-inch (10.2- × 20.3- × 40.6-cm) solid cap blocks, laid with the longest side running north and south, to construct a 16-inch-thick (40.6-cm) Trombe wall.

■ If wall is not in direct sunlight, it can be constructed of 4-inch-thick (10.2-cm) solid or filled concrete block or brick, with insulation on the outside.

■ Insulate the outside of a thermal storage wall with at least 4 inches (10.2 cm) of styrofoam beadboard bonded directly to the wall with construction adhesive and "stick clips"—galvanized spikes with a 2-inch-square (5-cm), perforated head that can be glued directly to the masonry wall. Stick clips have a galvanized metal disk that slides over the pointed end of the spike to hold the styrofoam insulation board in place. A styrofoam over masonry wall can be finished with a coat of adhesive mortar, fiberglass mesh, and stucco, using a system such as Dryvit (see Appendix D).

Or masonry walls can be insulated on the outside with three or four layers of 1-inch (2.5-cm) R-10 rigid insulation board, spaced with furring strips between them. The first layer next to the masonry wall should be foil faced, with the foil facing toward the interior of the house to act as a vapor and radiant barrier.

Or cover the masonry wall with builder's foil and build a 2- by 4-inch (5- × 10.2-cm) stud-frame wall *outside* the masonry wall; insulate between studs with fiberglass batts or cut 4-inch-thick (10.2-cm) styrofoam beadboard to fit snugly between the studs; cover the outside of the studs with a 1-inch (2.5-cm) layer of R-10 insulated sheathing and apply siding materials to match the remainder of the house.

Stud-Frame Walls

■ Use 2- by 6-inch (5- × 15.2-cm) studs for walls to allow space for R-19 fiberglass insulation batts; cover outside of studs with R-10 insulated sheathing board and siding. *Or* use 2- by 4-inch (5- × 10.2-cm) studs and insulate the wall with 3½-inch (8.9-cm) R-11 fiberglass batts with a vapor barrier; then apply two layers of 1-inch (2.5-cm) R-10 insulation board on outside of studs, spaced with furring strips. Cover wall with siding. (This is also a good way to add insulation to an existing 2- by 4-inch (5- × 10.2-cm) stud-frame wall if it is feasible to remove and replace existing siding.) *Or* build two 2- by 4-inch (5- × 10.2-cm) stud-frame walls, 8 to 10 inches (20.3 to 25.4 cm) apart, and fill the air space between the walls with loose fill (poured or blown) insulation material, such as mineral wool.

Roof (Cathedral or Vaulted Ceilings)

■ Use 2- by 8-inch or 2- by 10-inch (5- × 20.3-cm or 5- × 25.4-cm) rafters to allow space for R-30 fiberglass insulation blankets. Use a continuous 6-mil polyethylene film for a vapor barrier; apply to the underside of the rafters and continue down walls, overlapping edges to cover entire inner surface of walls and ceiling. The interior finish material (sheetrock, wood, or whatever) is applied directly over continuous vapor barrier. *Or* use 2- by 6-inch (5- × 15.2-cm) rafters with R-19 fiberglass insulation blankets and a continuous vapor barrier; then add two or

three layers of 1-inch (2.5-cm) R-10 insulation board spaced with furring strips.

■ Allow 1-inch (2.5-cm) air space between insulation and roof decking to allow heated air under roof surface to escape to the outside through a continuous ridge vent along the roofline.

HOW IT COULD BE: PLAN C (REBUILD)

For rebuilding projects, use the construction details from the previous sections of the chapter that apply to your specific project. For example, if the project will include a Trombe wall, refer to the relevant details under that section. For general details, refer to the descriptions included in the previous section, "Solar Additions."

GETTING ON WITH IT

Let us assume that you have now completed your retrofit project. Now what? Well . . . it is time to get on with living—naturally. The next chapter contains some advice on how to do that.

6.

Living with It: An Owner's Manual

Congratulations! You have made a wise investment in your energy future—one that will pay many dividends in the years ahead. The fact that you have made this expenditure in order to use the primary source of renewable energy, the sun, is indicative of your high level of intelligence and good judgment.

You are probably cheating a bit by reading this manual before you complete your retrofit, but no one could blame you. In fact, it would probably be to your advantage to read the owner's manual of anything that has an owner's manual before you decide to purchase it so you know what you are getting into.

So read on, but keep this manual handy as a reference and read it from time to time after you complete your retrofit.

WARRANTY INFORMATION

If the passive solar features of your house have been designed and built in accordance with the concepts and construction details contained in this book, they should operate efficiently (and quietly) when the sun is shining. The percentage of the total heating and cooling load of your house that is provided by the solar features will depend on the size and type of passive system you have built, the angle and orientation toward south of solar collector areas, the amount and type of thermal storage mass, the overall thermal efficiency (or heat loss) of your house, the percentage of

possible sunshine your area receives, and the number of heating and cooling degree days in your area.

The passive solar heating features of your house will provide a limited amount of heat when weather conditions are "cloudy and bright," but as a general rule, it is best not to expect to receive any heat from the sun when it is not visible. Any heat stored in thermal mass during sunny periods will, of course, be available for use at night and during cloudy periods. If the system has no thermal storage mass, it will work only when the sun is shining.

GENERAL OPERATING INSTRUCTIONS

The passive solar features of your house are basically self-operating, but your assistance will be necessary to achieve optimum performance from the system. Your major task is to control heat gain and loss within the solar collector areas and to regulate airflow. This is accomplished by raising and lowering insulating/reflective curtains, shades, or shutters over south-facing glazing; by opening and closing vents between the solar collector areas and the living spaces; and by opening and closing vents between the collector areas and the outdoors. Most of these regulatory functions can be done manually or by the use of automated devices that can be installed to operate vents and movable insulation.

SPECIFIC OPERATING INSTRUCTIONS

SOUTH-FACING WINDOWS

Heating: Open insulating curtains, shades, or shutters when the sun first illuminates the window(s) in the morning. Close curtains, shades, or shutters in late afternoon or early evening on sunny days and during the daytime in extremely overcast or stormy weather.

Cooling: If windows are not fully shaded by trees, a roof overhang, or a trellis, close insulating/reflective curtains, shades, or shutters during time when direct sun strikes windows. Open ventilating section of window at night to admit cooler night air; close windows during hottest part of the day.

ROOF WINDOWS OR SKYLIGHTS

Heating: Cover interior surface of glazing area with rigid insulation board or insulating shutters at night and during extremely overcast or stormy days. Remove insulation (open shutters) when sun is high enough to shine into interior of house.

Cooling: Open roof windows or skylights day and night (except during thunderstorms!) to allow hot air to escape from the interior of the house. If roof windows or skylights are in direct sunshine during the cooling season, install a reflective screening material, such as greenhouse shade cloth, to keep out sunlight and insects.

SOLAR COLLECTOR WINDOWS

Heating: When the morning sun fully illuminates collector window, open the top and bottom of interior window sash. Close window completely when sun is not striking it in late afternoon and during the daytime in overcast or stormy weather. Tilt dark upper surface of venetian blind toward the sun during sunny days; allow a small gap between blind slats to admit light and permit airflow. Close blinds completely at night and during overcast and stormy periods, with dark surface facing outdoors.

Cooling: Collector window must be shaded during the cooling season by trees, roof overhang, trellis, awning, roll-down shade, or other device. Top of exterior window and bottom of interior window sash should remain open day and night, except during inclement weather. Tilt light-colored undersurface of venetian blind toward sun; allow small gap between blind slats to admit light and permit airflow.

THERMOSIPHONING AIR PANEL (TAP)

Heating: TAPs work automatically in the heating mode and do not require any attention if they have back-draft dampers in the lower vent that open into the TAP. (It is necessary, however, to clean the exterior of the glazing surface of the TAP periodically).

Cooling: TAPs must be fully shaded during the cooling season unless they are equipped with registers with dampers over the high vents to the house and/or high vents between the TAP and the outdoors. If TAP has a high exterior vent, it should be left open during the cooling season.

WINDOW BOX HEATER

Heating: A window box heater works automatically in the heating mode and does not require any attention; nor does it require a back-draft damper, since cold air will settle at the bottom of the box at night. If the heater is equipped with a hinged flap or damper over its interior opening, open the flap or damper in the morning on sunny days and close it at night, during overcast and stormy periods, and during the cooling season. Clean the exterior of the window box heater glazing surface periodically.

Cooling: Remove and store the window box heater during the cooling season if possible, or cover the glazing surface to protect it from direct sunlight if the heater is not fully shaded by trees and must be left in place during the summer.

THERMAL STORAGE WALLS (TROMBE WALLS AND WATERWALLS)

Heating: Vented thermal storage walls work automatically in the heating mode if they have back-draft dampers in the low vents to prevent cold air from entering the living space at night. Unvented thermal storage walls also operate automatically by conduction and reradiation of heat stored in the wall. The exterior surface of the glazing on thermal storage walls must be cleaned periodically—at least once or twice a month during the heating season. If night insulation, such as a roll-down insulating/reflective shade, is used between the glazing and the thermal mass, it should be in the raised position while direct sunlight strikes the wall and should

be lowered at night and during the daytime in overcast and stormy weather.

Cooling: The glazing area of thermal storage walls must be fully shaded during the cooling season by trees, a roof overhang, awning, insulating/reflective shade, or other device. Exterior vents at the top of the glazing system should be open throughout the cooling season, except during inclement weather, to allow hot air to escape. (These vents must have an insect screen.) The south-facing glazing system for a freestanding waterwall should have screened high and low vents, such as awning windows that open to the outdoors. These vents should be opened during the night to cool the water in containers and closed in the daytime during extremely hot weather.

ATTACHED SOLAR STRUCTURES (GREENHOUSES, SUNSPACES, AND SOLAR PORCHES)

Heating: Install thermometers in the house and in the solar structure. When the temperature in the solar structure is warmer than the interior of the house, open windows, doors, and other vents between the house and the solar structure. When the temperature in the solar structure is lower than in the house, close them. If no one will be home during the day, look at the sky when you are ready to leave for the day, listen to the weather forecast, and take your best guess as to whether it will be sunny or cloudy during the day. If you think it will be sunny, open the vents before you leave, even though it may still be cooler in the solar structure than it is in the house. If you are uncertain about the weather or if you think it will be overcast, leave the vents, doors, or windows closed. It is usually best to close all openings between the house and the solar structure if you will be away from home for an extended period of time. This is especially true if the house has an uninsulated masonry wall between the living space and the solar structure. The glazing area of the solar structure should be insulated at night and during overcast or stormy weather to reduce heat loss through the glazing.

Note: The temperature in a well-designed and well-built attached solar structure should not fall below 40° to 45°F (4.4° to 7.2°C), nor should it get warmer than 90°–95°F (32.2° to 35°C) during the heating season. If the temperature does not consistently stay within this range—except during extreme weather conditions—more thermal storage mass, such as phase change materials or water in containers, should be added to the interior of the solar structure. The air in the structure should never get so hot during the heating season that it would be necessary to open exterior vents and thereby waste excess heat.

Cooling: The glazing area of an attached solar structure should be fully shaded during warm weather by trees, roll-down insulating/reflective shades, or other interior or exterior shading devices. High and low screened vents to the exterior can remain open day and night during the cooling season in most climates. Doors leading from the solar structure to the outdoors can usually be left open during the cooling season if a screen door is installed to keep insects out.

manufacture. You will save much frustration, money, and your own renewable energy by buying good-quality window-cleaning equipment and a professional-grade solvent. If you do not want to purchase such supplies, use vinegar and water as a solvent and dry the glazing with newspaper.

The other maintenance task that should be performed at least twice a year is checking the caulking around glazing areas for signs of deterioration and leakage. Any cracked or damaged caulking should be replaced to ensure an air- and watertight seal around the glazing. Painted surfaces of your passive solar features should also be checked regularly and repainted as necessary to protect the wood. If you use fiberglass glazing, it must be recoated with resin every few years to prevent deterioration and reduction of light transmission.

Mechanical features of your system, such as fans, controls, or automated devices, should also be checked regularly and maintained in accordance with manufacturers' recommendations.

MAINTENANCE

The major components of your passive solar features are essentially maintenance-free. In fact, the only regular maintenance required for most of the passive solar options described in this book is to periodically clean the solar collector areas (south-facing glazing). It is especially important to keep the glazing clean during the heating season, since any dirt or film allowed to accumulate on the glazing area will reduce the efficiency of the system. Professional-grade window-washing equipment, such as a squeegee with an extension handle and a washing brush, which can be purchased from a janitorial supply firm, will greatly simplify your window-cleaning chores. Forget about using a spray-type window cleaner and paper towels; these products and their containers require a great deal of nonrenewable energy to

RECORD KEEPING

Although it would seem logical to use lower fuel bills as the criterion to determine the effectiveness of your solar retrofit project, this approach does not account for the rapid escalation in the cost of nonrenewable energy. (At the time of this writing, fuel costs were rising at a rate of approximately 35 percent per year!). It is possible, for example, that your actual dollar expenditure for heating and cooling would *increase* from year to year, even though your house uses less energy as a result of a solar retrofit. So in addition to looking at the cost factors, it is important to monitor the actual amount of energy used to heat and cool your house before and after your retrofit is completed.

Suppose, for example, you want to compare your energy usage for the winters before and after completing your retrofit. The actual dollar expenditure for energy during the two winters could be compared directly but would have to be adjusted for inflation. Comparing meter readings between the two winters would not tell the whole story either unless you also compared the number of heating degree days for each winter. (The actual number of degree days in your area is published in the monthly bulletin *Local Climatological Conditions*, available from the National Climatic Center. See Appendix D for ordering information.) If you want to get somewhat scientific about your comparison, divide the total degree days for the heating season by the total number of units of energy used—gallons of heating oil or liquid propane, kilowatts of electricity, cubic feet (steres) of natural gas, or cords of firewood—during the heating season. This long division problem will result in a cost-per-degree-day factor that can be compared with subsequent years. Such a comparison would of course assume that you maintained a similar temperature range within your house over the two winters being compared.

In addition to performing the kind of mathematical gymnastics described above, you or someone else in your household may be interested in keeping temperature charts to monitor the performance of your house with its newly added solar features. The first step in such a monitoring program would be to install a maximum-minimum thermometer outdoors, preferably on the north side of your house, so that you can keep records of the daily high and low ambient temperatures. Such thermometers could also be installed in the main living areas of the house and in the greenhouse, sunspace, or solar porch, if you have one. With these thermometers in place, a simple chart such as the one in figure 6-1 can be kept on a daily or weekly basis. In addition to recording the temperatures, you may want to monitor the use of externally supplied energy by recording the meter readings. You might also want to keep track of the general sky conditions and your thermostat setting if you use conventional heating in addition to solar, or the quantity and type of firewood you use if you are burning wood for auxiliary heat.

Keeping records year-round is important if

you want to assess the contribution of your solar features in both the heating and cooling modes. In fact, if your solar collector areas are not well shaded, it could turn out that the money you saved during the winter is burned up in air-conditioning costs in the summer! If you keep records, you will know exactly what is happening.

What might be the value of the kind of record keeping and cost analysis described above? It could provide a healthy outlet for you if you like to make charts and graphs and use your calculator, but the real reasons would be so that you can actually see the value of your investment increase as the years go by and so that you can make adjustments or additions to your passive solar system to improve its efficiency. Without records you can only guess what is happening, and you may be subject to errors in judgments brought about by a strong desire to believe you have made a sound investment. An interesting but somewhat sad case in point is that some inhabitants of homes with solar features unconsciously become more wasteful, for example, leaving lights on or maintaining a higher thermostat setting, because they believe they are already doing their part to save energy by living in a solar house. This is absurd: we should save energy so we can waste it?

The folklore surrounding solar houses is currently at a level similar to where the Volkswagen was in the late fifties and early sixties. All of us can recall at least one owner of an early model VW who made exaggerated claims about the fuel efficiency of the vehicle—perhaps to justify the size and overall appearance of the automobile. We also heard the stories about the guy who would add gasoline to his neighbor's VW—and later siphon gasoline from it—just to fuel and later discredit the owner's claims of tremendous gas mileage.

This same kind of folklore seems to apply to many owners of homes with solar features who are eager to justify the value of their investment in solar energy. Rather than perpetuate this kind of folklore, it would be better to keep actual records so that you can document for yourself, your neighbors and friends, your mother-in-law, or anyone else who wants to

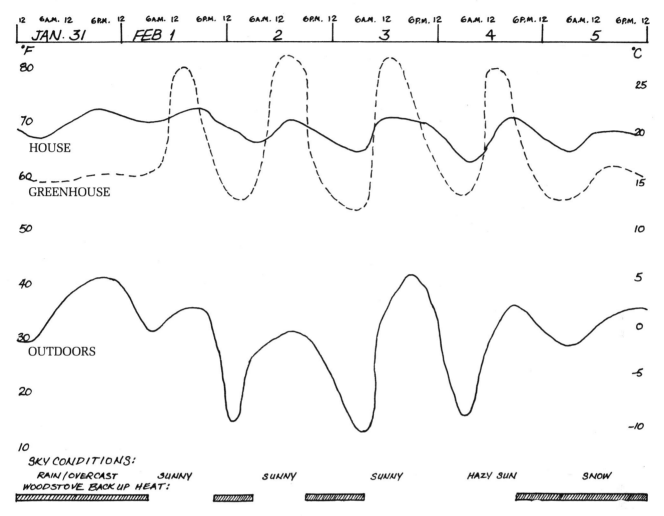

6.1. Temperature chart (actual readings from a retrofitted passive solar house, February, 1981)

know, the actual value of your investment. If you keep in mind that millions of homes could be retrofitted, you may come to believe that you have a responsibility to supply other home-owners with hard data, not folklore, to help convince them of the feasibility and value of solar retrofitting.

AUXILIARY HEATING, COOLING, AND AIR DISTRIBUTION DEVICES

After you have had an opportunity to check the performance of the passive solar features of your house in both heating and cooling modes,

you may decide that one or more of the following devices would be a good investment for your comfort and convenience.

WOOD-BURNING STOVES

Many owners of solar homes use wood as a primary or sole source of backup heat for cold, cloudy days when sufficient sunshine is not available to heat their homes. This makes a great deal of sense, since wood is a renewable energy resource that is readily available in most areas.

Availability of Firewood

In order for wood to be feasible as a fuel for backup heating, it must be available at a reasonable price or free for the cutting. This is not the case in most urban areas—which is probably fortunate from the standpoint of air quality. (Can you imagine what it would be like if everyone in a given city block or suburban development were to burn wood at the same time? If you have ever stayed at a campground where a cozy campfire roared at every campsite in the evening, you understand the point.) Many homeowners who have installed expensive wood-burning stoves in areas where firewood is sold at the local convenience-food store at a cost of two logs for ninety-nine cents have discovered that the price of firewood has risen almost as sharply as conventional fuels, thus eroding the economic value of their investment in wood burning.

Before you make a final decision on whether to use wood as a source of backup heat, check the availability of firewood in your area. Although seasoned hardwoods have the highest heat-producing potential, a mixture of unseasoned and seasoned wood can be burned at the same time and some softer woods that burn rapidly can be used for quick heating when starting up a wood-burning stove.

Many people who start out with the stuff of which the road to hell is paved, that is, good intentions of cutting their own firewood, quickly change their minds after a few hours of ear-splitting, blister-raising, back-breaking work. If the economic feasibility of using wood as fuel depends on your cutting your own wood rather than buying it, try cutting and splitting wood for a day before you make a decision.

Purchasing a Wood-Burning Stove

In addition to the environmental issues and the availability of reasonably priced, good-quality firewood, the question of whether to use wood as backup heat comes down to deciding if you want (or can afford) to spend $800 to $1500 for a top-of-the-line airtight or catalytic wood-burning stove and the cost of having it installed properly. You can, of course, purchase a less expensive stove and install it yourself at about half the cost ($400 to $750) of more efficient stoves, but as a general rule, inexpensive stoves are not a sound investment. This is particularly

6-2. Airtight wood-burning stove installed next to masonry wall with stack rising straight up (Photo: Darryl Strickler)

true if you must pay for your firewood. The heat-producing efficiency and durability of a given stove should be the primary considerations; it is generally true that more efficient stoves are more expensive. If you decide to purchase a wood-burning stove, buy one that has a sufficient BTU rating to heat the area you need to heat. In most climates a stove rated at 85,000 BTUs per hour will adequately heat a well-insulated 2,000-square-foot (185.8-ca) house if the house has sufficient airflow between rooms. Keep in mind, however, that the performance of a given stove will vary greatly depending on the type of wood being burned, the rate of burn, the draft conditions, and the amount of creosote buildup in the stove and chimney.

Installing A Wood-Burning Stove

A wood-burning stove should be installed as close to the center of the house as possible so that it can provide radiant and convective heat to the entire house. If the stove can be located near a masonry wall, as shown in figure 6-2, the wall will absorb and reradiate stored heat. Also, a masonry wall is obviously fireproof, whereas a wood-frame wall near a stove can be a significant fire hazard if the wall is not adequately protected by a fireproof shield between the stove and the wall.

The fewer twists and turns (elbows) the stovepipe stack has, the better. A stack with more turns is subject to more creosote buildup than a straight stack, and a stack that rises through the living space is preferable to one that rises outside the wall of the house because the stack will heat the air around it. Therefore, the most desirable installation is to place the stove so that the stack rises straight up from the stove and out through the roof. As an added advantage to installing the stove near the center of the house with the stack rising through the roof, you can take down and store the interior sections of the stack during the cooling season and then fit the top of the stack extension that rises above the roof with a wind turbine (and insect screen) to exhaust hot air from the house.

Many people who purchase wood-burning stoves install them through the opening of an existing fireplace. This is not usually advisable because of the number of elbows required in the stack and because of the problem of creosote buildup inside the existing fireplace and chimney. Here, regular cleaning to reduce the fire hazard associated with creosote buildup becomes very important. A straight stack is much easier to clean than a fireplace smoke chamber.

A final word of caution with regard to installing a wood-burning stove is warranted. Unless you are absolutely certain that you can install a wood-burning stove so that it does not become a fire hazard, have an experienced professional install it for you. The cost of installation will be far less than the cost of replacing your house.

Stove Accessories

A pair of fireproof gloves can come in very handy when loading a stove that is already burning. A specially designed thermometer that attaches to the stovepipe stack will allow you

to monitor the temperature of the stack and keep it within the safety range. An overheated stack can ignite the creosote built up in the stack, and an underheated stack can increase the likelihood of creosote buildup.

You might also consider using a small heat recovery fan that attaches to the stack and distributes the hot air from the stack around adjacent living space. And finally, you might consider making or buying a water jacket to install around your wood-burning stove to heat domestic hot water during the winter months. Water heated in this way can be used directly, or it can supply a conventional hot water heater with preheated water.

CEILING FANS

If you have rooms with high ceilings or with vaulted or cathedral ceilings, warmer air will collect and stagnate at the ceiling level. Unless you want to string a hammock across the top of the ceiling and sleep in it, most of this heat will be wasted. Warm air at the ceiling level creates a greater push against the insulation in the ceiling in its attempt to sneak out through the roof. Therefore, some means to return the warm air to the living spaces below is necessary.

Enter, or reenter, that old-time wonder, the ceiling fan (sometimes called a paddle fan),

6-3. Electrically reversible, variable-speed ceiling fan (Photo: Darryl Strickler)

which operates on just pennies—make that nickels and dimes—per day. The fact that ceiling fans have become a sort of fad does not in the least alter their potential to assist with the heating and cooling of your house—provided, of course, that you select one that can do the job. Such a fan should not only be able to prevent hot air from stagnating at the ceiling level during the heating season, it should also be able to assist with the evacuation of hot air through roof vents, skylights, or roof windows during the cooling season. And it should be able to provide cooling breezes indoors when nothing is stirring outdoors. (You can, in fact, create quite a turbulence indoors by installing two electrically reversible fans in a large open area of the house by running one fan so that it blows downward while the other draws air upward.) Literally thousands of models of ceiling fans are on the market today. In fact, there are even large retail stores in many areas that sell nothing but ceiling fans and related accessories. With such a variety to choose from, selecting the most efficient and effective fan can be a bewildering experience indeed. Beyond the question of what you want your fan to look like—a choice of mind-boggling proportions in itself—the major criteria for selecting a fan should be that it have an electrically reversible motor, variable speed controls, and large cooling vents on the motor housing. Although this is not always the case, fans with sealed motors generally have a shorter life expectancy. As is the case with most items you purchase, if you buy something cheap, you get something that *is* cheap. A good 52-inch (132-cm) ceiling fan will cost $200 or more but is a worthwhile investment. In fact, many ceiling fans of the old-fashioned variety are still in use after more than fifty years of paddling along. The ones in *Casablanca*, Bogie's film classic, are probably still working—somewhere.

AIR DESTRATIFICATION JETS

If you refuse to buy ceiling fans simply because they are too trendy for your tastes, you might consider installing air destratification jets to prevent hot air from stagnating at the ceiling

6-4. Strato-Jet™ air destratification jet (Photo: Courtesy of Rusth Industries)

level. These simple, mushroom-shaped devices operate quietly on a minimum amount of electricity, sending a gentle stream of air wafting gently downward. (Sound pretty poetic, don't they?) Commercially available models such as the Strato-Jet™ (see Appendix D for manufacturer's address) cost less than $80 in 1981. They can be hung from a ceiling and plugged into an electrical outlet, thus eliminating the need to wire them directly into the house current. Reversible ceiling fans do, however, have the added advantage of assisting with cooling, while destratification jets are primarily useful only during the heating season.

REGULATORY DEVICES AND DUCT FANS

If you wish to have mechanical devices control some of the regulatory functions of your otherwise passive system, you might consider using passively operated "heat motors" to open and close vents. These simple mechanical devices operate automatically (without electricity) to open and close vents at predetermined temperature settings, thus regulating airflow between the house and a greenhouse, for example (see Appendix D for manufacturers' addresses).

Electrically operated motors, controlled by temperature- or light-sensing devices, can also be used to operate vents, fans, or insulating curtains. These items allow *you* to be more passive, but they take some of the fun out of regulating your own living environment.

Low-volume, thermostatically controlled duct fans can be used to extract hot air from an attached solar structure—either to living spaces or outdoors depending on the season of the year.

DECORATING AND FURNISHING PASSIVE SOLAR SPACES

If your retrofit involved adding an attached solar structure or direct gain features to your present living space, you may want to consider the following information on a selection and arrangement of furnishings.

FLOORS

Do *not* carpet concrete floors that are struck by direct sunlight if they are intended to serve as thermal storage mass. Use area rugs or woven mats if you wish, but leave at least 70 to 75 percent of the total floor area uncovered. Try to place rugs or mats on the part of the floor that receives the least amount of direct sunlight in winter and the greatest amount of direct sunlight in summer. Rearrange the placement of the rugs and other furnishings to correspond to the seasonal variation in the area of the floor struck by the sun.

6-5. Heat-Motor™ self-operating vent opener (Photo: Courtesy of Heat Motors Distributing)

WALLS

If walls are constructed of masonry material and are in direct sunlight, do not use wall hangings or pictures that cover a large area of the wall surface. Also do not place wall hangings or large pictures on the interior surface of a thermal storage wall such as the room side of a Trombe wall or the interior surface of a masonry wall that separates a greenhouse or sunspace from the house.

Paint interior masonry walls a medium to light color so that these walls will reflect sunlight to the dark-colored masonry floors. Ceilings and walls of wood-frame construction should be painted a very light color to improve reflectance. Concrete floors in a greenhouse,

6-6. Interior of solarium, Pfister residence (PCM thermal storage rods visible in window at right) (Photo: Franz C. Hall)

sunspace, or solar porch can be painted or stained a dark, reddish brown to improve absorption. The red tint will also reflect light from the red end of the color spectrum back to plants in these areas, which is important for their growth.

FURNITURE

Any furniture placed in a greenhouse, sunspace, or living area that is in direct sunlight should have the least possible amount of surface area and mass so that the furniture will not shade thermal storage mass in walls and floors and will not block the flow of radiant heat from the storage mass. The furniture placed in these areas should have light-colored fabrics, which are less susceptible to fading. For example, director's chairs with white or tan canvas seats and a lightweight (low-mass) wooden table would be preferable to a dark-colored, heavily padded traditional dining room set, and metal-frame canvas sling chairs would be preferable to overstuffed furniture in a direct gain area. A simple guideline would be to keep furniture light in weight and light in color. Otherwise it will shade the floors and walls and will fade.

6-7. Kitchen and first floor of solarium in Pfister residence (note quarry tile floor and reflective ceiling in kitchen)
(Photo: Franz C. Hall)

AIR QUALITY OF PASSIVE SOLAR HOMES

This section contains miscellaneous concepts, facts, and suggestions related to the air quality of homes like yours that have passive solar features.

MAKING SCENTS

Consider for a moment the side of your house that is struck by the prevailing spring and summer breezes. Your house should have windows or low vents on this side to catch these breezes. Why not plant the flowers or bushes that produce your favorite fragrance in front of these vents or windows? How about planting lilies of the valley in front of the low vents under the glazing of a greenhouse? What about a lilac bush under the window? If you are a person who likes the smell of geraniums, why not plant some in front of inlet vents or windows, or even inside your greenhouse or sunspace? The possibilities are limited only by what you can imagine and by what you like to smell.

DUST AND OTHER UFOs

Allergy specialists who have analyzed the quality of the air inside typical houses have discovered that it is heavily laden with dust and other particulate and chemical matter that is downright unhealthy to breathe. Carpeting, drapes, and stuffed furniture are the primary culprits for producing, collecting, and storing dust; natural gas and propane cookstoves and furnaces release fumes from incomplete combustion; paints, sealants, household cleaning agents, and some types of insulation release noxious gases; the list goes on and on. No matter how well and how often you clean, it is virtually impossible to bring a typically furnished home even close to sanitary standards.

Behold the solar house (or solar addition): no carpeting—instead, quarry tile floors that can be *washed*; no drapes—roll-down insulating curtains that are rolled up at least half of the time; no stuffed furniture to shade the floors and collect and produce dust; no oil furnace to give off fumes, and so on. A much healthier environment for people and plants, yes?

H_2O, O_2, AND YOU

Speaking of plants, you should have as many in your home as you can afford and take care of. Not only do they add beauty, they also add moisture and oxygen to the air in your home—both of which are necessary to good health in humans. A solar-heated home with a sunspace full of plants usually has a much higher moisture content than a home heated by forced hot air, for example. This is particularly helpful during the heating season and in dry climates. And, although it is not yet a documented fact, it is probable that solar home dwellers suffer fewer "dry air ills" and cold-related sickness than do the inhabitants of conventionally heated homes.

PASSIVE SOLAR: SCIENCE OR MAGIC?

Whether they could actually explain them or not, people all over the world have understood the scientific principles of passive solar application for thousands of years. In recent years practical applications of passive solar for heating and cooling have been evaluated, analyzed, and documented, with this conclusion: it works! For some people the question of *how* it works is less important than the fact that it does work. These people prefer to think of passive solar as a form of magic. No matter how scientifically inclined you are, a time may come when you may begin to view passive solar as magic. Perhaps it will come on a cold January morning when the sun has heated your house "all by itself," or maybe it will be on a hot afternoon

6-8. Interior of sunspace in Metz residence (fiberglass water storage columns at right) (Photo: Harriet Wise)

in August when your house is cooled by the summer breeze rather than a noisy air conditioner. If, or when, that time comes, you will know it. For now, keep believing—we could all use a little more magic in our lives.

PASSIVE SOLAR LIFE STYLES FOR ACTIVE LIVING

So there you are in your recently retrofitted home. Now what? What can you expect in addition to reduced consumption of nonrenewable energy resources and perhaps a coupon booklet for loan repayments? How could your new sunspace change the way you live? What would a soak in a solar-heated hot tub (that also serves as thermal storage) do to calm your jangled nerves after a day in the city? How would staying at home to do your work instead of going to the office change your life? How will your closer attention to the weather and the sun change the way you perceive the world and your own connection with nature?

The answers to these questions are, of course, yours to discover.

> May you enjoy the discovering,
> May the sun always rise to greet you,
> May the wind be always at your back, and . . .
> May you view the future brightly—with new perspective—through your south-facing glazing.

Appendix A: Weather Data

NORMAL TOTAL HEATING DEGREE DAYS
(Base 65°)

STATE AND STATION	JULY	AUG.	SEP.	OCT.	NOV.	DEC.	JAN.	FEB.	MAR.	APR.	MAY	JUNE	ANNUAL
ALA. BIRMINGHAM	0	0	6	93	363	555	592	462	363	108	9	0	2551
HUNTSVILLE	0	0	12	127	426	663	694	557	434	138	19	0	3070
MOBILE	0	0	0	22	213	357	415	300	211	42	0	0	1560
MONTGOMERY	0	0	0	68	330	527	543	417	316	90	0	0	2291
ALASKA ANCHORAGE	245	291	516	930	1284	1572	1631	1316	1293	879	592	315	10864
ANNETTE	242	208	327	567	738	899	949	837	843	648	490	321	7069
BARROW	803	840	1035	1500	1971	2362	2517	2332	2468	1944	1445	957	20174
BARTER IS.	735	775	987	1482	1944	2337	2536	2369	2477	1923	1373	924	19862
BETHEL	319	394	612	1042	1434	1866	1903	1590	1655	1173	806	402	13196
COLD BAY	474	425	525	772	918	1122	1153	1036	1122	951	791	591	9880
CORDOVA	366	391	522	781	1017	1221	1299	1086	1113	864	660	444	9764
FAIRBANKS	171	332	642	1203	1833	2254	2359	1901	1739	1068	555	222	14279
JUNEAU	301	338	483	725	921	1135	1237	1070	1073	810	601	381	9075
KING SALMON	313	322	513	908	1290	1606	1600	1333	1411	966	673	408	11343
KOTZEBUE	381	446	723	1249	1728	2127	2192	1932	2080	1554	1057	636	16105
MCGRATH	208	338	633	1184	1791	2232	2294	1817	1758	1122	648	258	14283
NOME	481	496	693	1094	1455	1820	1879	1666	1770	1314	930	573	14171
SAINT PAUL	605	539	612	862	963	1197	1228	1168	1265	1098	936	726	11199
SHEMYA	577	475	501	784	876	1042	1045	958	1011	885	837	696	9687
YAKUTAT	338	347	474	716	936	1144	1169	1019	1042	840	632	435	9092
ARIZ. FLAGSTAFF	46	68	201	558	867	1073	1169	991	911	651	437	180	7152
PHOENIX	0	0	0	22	234	415	474	328	217	75	0	0	1765
PRESCOTT	0	0	27	245	579	797	865	711	605	360	158	15	4362
TUCSON	0	0	0	25	231	406	471	344	242	75	6	0	1800
WINSLOW	0	0	6	245	711	1008	1054	770	601	291	96	0	4782
YUMA	0	0	0	0	148	319	363	228	130	29	0	0	1217
ARK. FORT SMITH	0	0	12	127	450	704	781	596	456	144	22	0	3292
LITTLE ROCK	0	0	9	127	465	716	756	577	434	126	9	0	3219
TEXARKANA	0	0	0	78	345	561	626	468	350	105	0	0	2533
CALIF. BAKERSFIELD	0	0	0	37	282	502	546	364	267	105	19	0	2122
BISHOP	0	0	42	248	576	797	874	666	539	306	143	36	4227
BLUE CANYON	34	50	120	347	579	766	865	781	791	582	397	195	5507
BURBANK	0	0	6	43	177	301	366	277	239	138	81	18	1646
EUREKA	270	257	258	329	414	499	546	470	505	438	372	285	4643
FRESNO	0	0	0	78	339	558	586	406	319	150	56	0	2492
LONG BEACH	0	0	12	40	156	288	375	297	267	168	90	18	1711
LOS ANGELES	28	22	42	78	180	291	372	302	288	219	158	81	2061
MT. SHASTA	25	34	123	406	696	902	983	784	738	525	347	159	5722
OAKLAND	53	50	45	127	309	481	527	400	353	255	180	90	2870
POINT ARGUELLO	202	186	162	205	291	400	474	392	403	339	298	243	3595
RED BLUFF	0	0	0	53	318	555	605	428	341	168	47	0	2515
SACRAMENTO	0	0	12	81	363	577	614	442	360	216	102	6	2773
SANDBERG	0	0	30	202	480	691	778	661	620	426	264	57	4209
SAN DIEGO	6	0	15	37	123	251	313	249	202	123	84	36	1439
SAN FRANCISCO	81	78	60	143	306	462	508	395	363	279	214	126	3015
SANTA CATALINA	16	0	9	50	165	279	353	308	326	249	192	105	2052
SANTA MARIA	99	93	96	146	270	391	459	370	363	282	233	165	2967
COLO. ALAMOSA	65	99	279	639	1065	1420	1476	1162	1020	696	440	168	8529
COLORADO SPRINGS	9	25	132	456	825	1032	1128	938	893	582	319	84	6423
DENVER	6	9	117	428	819	1035	1132	938	887	558	288	66	6283
GRAND JUNCTION	0	0	30	313	786	1113	1209	907	729	387	146	21	5641
PUEBLO	0	0	54	326	750	986	1085	871	772	429	174	15	5462
CONN. BRIDGEPORT	0	0	66	307	615	986	1079	966	853	510	208	27	5617
HARDFORT	0	6	99	372	711	1119	1209	1061	899	495	177	24	6172
NEW HAVEN	0	12	87	347	648	1011	1097	991	871	543	245	45	5897
DEL. WILMINGTON	0	0	51	270	588	927	980	874	735	387	112	6	4930
FLA. APALACHICOLA	0	0	0	16	153	319	347	260	180	33	0	0	1308
DAYTONA BEACH	0	0	0	0	75	211	248	190	140	15	0	0	879
FORT MYERS	0	0	0	0	24	109	146	101	62	0	0	0	442
JACKSONVILLE	0	0	0	12	144	310	332	246	174	21	0	0	1239
KEY WEST	0	0	0	0	0	28	40	31	9	0	0	0	108
LAKELAND	0	0	0	0	57	164	195	146	99	0	0	0	661
MIAMI BEACH	0	0	0	0	0	40	56	36	9	0	0	0	141
ORLANDO	0	0	0	0	72	198	220	165	105	6	0	0	766
PENSACOLA	0	0	0	19	195	353	400	277	183	36	0	0	1463
TALLAHASSEE	0	0	0	28	198	360	375	286	202	36	0	0	1485
TAMPA	0	0	0	0	60	171	202	148	102	0	0	0	683
WEST PALM BEACH	0	0	0	0	6	65	87	64	31	0	0	0	253
GA. ATHENS	0	0	12	115	405	632	642	529	431	141	22	0	2929
ATLANTA	0	0	18	127	414	626	639	529	437	168	25	0	2983
AUGUSTA	0	0	0	78	333	552	549	445	350	90	0	0	2397
COLUMBUS	0	0	0	78	333	543	552	434	338	96	0	0	2383
MACON	0	0	0	71	297	502	505	403	295	63	0	0	2136
ROME	0	0	24	161	474	701	710	577	468	177	34	0	3326
SAVANNAH	0	0	0	47	246	437	437	353	254	45	0	0	1819
THOMASVILLE	0	0	0	25	198	366	394	305	208	33	0	0	1529
IDAHO BOISE	0	0	132	415	792	1017	1113	854	722	438	245	81	5809
IDAHO FALLS 46W	16	34	270	623	1056	1370	1538	1249	1085	651	391	192	8475
IDAHO FALLS 42NW	16	40	282	648	1107	1432	1600	1291	1107	657	388	192	8760
LEWISTON	0	0	123	403	756	933	1063	815	694	426	239	90	5542
POCATELLO	0	0	172	493	900	1166	1324	1058	905	555	319	141	7033
ILL. CAIRO	0	0	36	164	513	791	856	680	539	195	47	0	3821
CHICAGO	0	0	81	326	753	1113	1209	1044	890	480	211	48	6155
MOLINE	0	9	99	335	774	1181	1314	1100	918	450	189	39	6408
PEORIA	0	6	87	326	759	1113	1218	1025	849	426	183	33	6025
ROCKFORD	6	9	114	400	837	1221	1333	1137	961	516	236	60	6830
SPRINGFIELD	0	0	72	291	696	1023	1135	935	769	354	136	18	5429
IND. EVANSVILLE	0	0	66	220	606	896	955	767	620	237	68	0	4435
FORT WAYNE	0	9	105	378	783	1135	1178	1028	890	471	189	39	6205
INDIANAPOLIS	0	0	90	316	723	1051	1113	949	809	432	177	39	5699
SOUTH BEND	0	6	111	372	777	1125	1221	1070	933	525	239	60	6439
IOWA Burlington	0	0	93	322	768	1135	1259	1042	859	426	177	33	6114
DES MOINES	0	9	99	363	837	1231	1398	1165	967	489	211	39	6808
DUBUQUE	12	31	156	450	906	1287	1420	1204	1026	546	260	78	7376
SIOUX CITY	0	9	108	369	867	1240	1435	1198	989	483	214	39	6951
WATERLOO	12	19	138	428	909	1296	1460	1221	1023	531	229	54	7320

NORMAL TOTAL HEATING DEGREE DAYS
(Base 65°)

STATE AND STATION	JULY	AUG.	SEP.	OCT.	NOV.	DEC.	JAN.	FEB.	MAR.	APR.	MAY	JUNE	ANNUAL
KANS. CONCORDIA	0	0	57	276	705	1023	1163	935	781	372	149	18	5479
DODGE CITY	0	0	33	251	666	939	1051	840	719	354	124	9	4986
GOODLAND	0	6	81	381	810	1073	1166	955	884	507	236	42	6141
TOPEKA	0	0	57	270	672	980	1122	893	722	330	124	12	5182
WICHITA	0	0	33	229	618	905	1023	804	645	270	87	6	4620
KY. COVINGTON	0	0	75	291	669	983	1035	893	756	390	149	24	5265
LEXINGTON	0	0	54	239	609	902	946	818	685	325	105	0	4683
LOUISVILLE	0	0	54	248	609	890	930	818	682	315	105	9	4660
LA. ALEXANDRIA	0	0	0	56	273	431	471	361	260	69	0	0	1921
BATON ROUGE	0	0	0	31	216	369	409	294	208	33	0	0	1560
BURRWOOD	0	0	0	0	96	214	298	218	171	27	0	0	1024
LAKE CHARLES	0	0	0	19	210	341	381	274	195	39	0	0	1459
NEW ORLEANS	0	0	0	19	192	322	363	258	192	39	0	0	1385
SHREVEPORT	0	0	0	47	297	477	552	426	304	81	0	0	2184
MAINE CARIBOU	78	115	336	682	1044	1535	1690	1470	1308	858	468	183	9767
PORTLAND	12	53	195	508	807	1215	1339	1182	1042	675	372	111	7511
MD. BALTIMORE	0	0	48	264	585	905	936	820	679	327	90	0	4654
FREDERICK	0	0	66	307	624	955	995	876	741	384	127	12	5087
MASS. BLUE HILL OBSY	0	22	108	381	690	1085	1178	1053	936	579	267	69	6368
BOSTON	0	9	60	316	603	983	1088	972	846	513	208	36	5634
NANTUCKET	12	22	93	332	573	896	992	941	896	621	384	129	5891
PITTSFIELD	25	59	219	524	831	1231	1339	1196	1063	660	326	105	7578
WORCESTER	6	34	147	450	774	1172	1271	1123	998	612	304	78	6969
MICH. ALPENA	68	105	273	580	912	1268	1404	1299	1218	777	446	156	8506
DETROIT (CITY)	0	0	87	360	738	1088	1181	1058	936	522	220	42	6232
ESCANABA	59	87	243	539	924	1293	1445	1296	1203	777	456	159	8481
FLINT	16	40	159	465	843	1212	1330	1198	1066	639	319	90	7377
GRAND RAPIDS	9	28	135	434	804	1147	1259	1134	1011	579	279	75	6894
LANSING	6	22	138	431	813	1163	1262	1142	1011	579	273	69	6909
MARQUETTE	59	81	240	527	936	1268	1411	1268	1187	771	468	177	8393
MUSKEGON	12	28	120	400	762	1088	1209	1100	995	594	310	78	6696
SAULT STE. MARIE	96	105	279	580	951	1367	1525	1380	1277	810	477	201	9048
MINN. DULUTH	71	109	330	632	1131	1581	1745	1518	1355	840	490	198	10000
INTERNATIONAL FALLS	71	112	363	701	1236	1724	1919	1621	1414	828	443	174	10606
MINNEAPOLIS	22	31	189	505	1014	1454	1631	1380	1166	621	288	81	8382
ROCHESTER	25	34	186	474	1005	1438	1593	1366	1150	630	301	93	8295
SAINT CLOUD	28	47	225	549	1065	1500	1702	1445	1221	666	326	105	8879
MISS. JACKSON	0	0	0	65	315	502	546	414	310	87	0	0	2239
MERIDIAN	0	0	0	81	339	518	543	417	310	81	0	0	2289
VICKSBURG	0	0	0	53	279	462	512	384	282	69	0	0	2041
MO. COLUMBIA	0	0	54	251	651	967	1076	874	716	324	121	12	5046
KANSAS	0	0	39	220	612	905	1032	818	682	294	109	0	4711
ST. JOSEPH	0	6	60	285	708	1039	1172	949	769	348	133	15	5484
ST. LOUIS	0	0	60	251	627	936	1026	848	704	312	121	15	4900
SPRINGFIELD	0	0	45	223	600	877	973	781	660	291	105	6	4561
MONT. BILLINGS	6	15	186	487	897	1135	1296	1100	970	570	285	102	7049
GLASGOW	31	47	270	608	1104	1466	1711	1439	1187	648	335	150	8996
GREAT FALLS	28	53	258	543	921	1169	1349	1154	1063	642	384	186	7750
HAVRE	28	53	306	595	1065	1367	1584	1364	1181	657	338	162	8700
HELENA	31	59	294	601	1002	1265	1438	1170	1042	651	381	195	8129
KALISPELL	50	99	321	654	1020	1240	1401	1134	1029	639	397	207	8191
MILES CITY	6	6	174	502	972	1296	1504	1252	1057	579	276	99	7723
MISSOULA	34	74	303	651	1035	1287	1420	1120	970	621	391	219	8125
NEBR. GRAND ISLAND	0	6	108	381	834	1172	1314	1089	908	462	211	45	6530
LINCOLN	0	6	75	301	726	1066	1237	1016	834	402	171	30	5864
NORFOLK	9	0	111	397	873	1234	1414	1179	983	498	233	48	6979
NORTH PLATTE	0	6	123	440	885	1166	1271	1039	930	519	248	57	6684
OMAHA	0	12	105	357	828	1175	1355	1126	939	465	208	42	6612
SCOTTSBLUFF	0	0	138	459	876	1128	1231	1008	921	552	285	75	6673
VALENTINE	9	12	165	493	942	1237	1395	1176	1045	579	288	84	7425
NEV. ELKO	9	34	225	561	924	1197	1314	1036	911	621	409	192	7433
ELY	28	43	234	592	939	1184	1308	1075	977	672	456	225	7733
LAS VEGAS	0	0	0	78	387	617	688	487	335	111	6	0	2709
RENO	43	87	204	490	801	1026	1073	823	729	510	357	189	6332
WINNEMUCCA	0	34	210	536	876	1091	1172	916	837	573	363	153	6761
N. H. CONCORD	6	50	177	505	822	1240	1358	1184	1032	636	298	75	7383
MT. WASH. OBSY.	493	536	720	1057	1341	1742	1820	1663	1652	1260	930	603	13817
N. J. ATLANTIC CITY	0	0	39	251	549	880	936	848	741	420	133	15	4812
NEWARK	0	0	30	248	573	921	983	876	729	381	118	0	4859
TRENTON	0	0	57	264	576	924	989	885	753	399	121	12	4980
N. MEX. ALBUQUERQUE	0	0	12	229	642	868	930	703	595	288	81	0	4348
CLAYTON	0	6	66	310	699	899	986	812	747	429	183	21	5158
RATON	9	28	126	431	825	1048	1116	904	834	543	301	63	6228
ROSWELL	0	0	18	202	573	806	840	641	481	201	31	0	3793
SILVER CITY	0	0	6	183	525	729	791	605	518	261	87	0	3705
N. Y. ALBANY	0	19	138	440	777	1194	1311	1156	992	564	239	45	6875
BINGHAMTON (AP)	22	65	201	471	810	1184	1277	1154	1045	645	313	99	7286
BINGHAMTON (PO)	0	28	141	406	732	1107	1190	1081	949	543	229	45	6451
BUFFALO	19	37	141	440	777	1156	1256	1145	1039	645	329	78	7062
CENTRAL PARK	0	0	30	233	540	902	986	885	760	408	118	9	4871
J. F. KENNEDY INTL.	0	0	36	248	564	933	1029	935	815	480	167	12	5219
LAGUARDIA	0	0	27	223	528	887	973	879	750	414	124	6	4811
ROCHESTER	9	31	126	415	747	1125	1234	1123	1014	597	279	48	6748
SCHENECTADY	0	22	123	422	756	1159	1283	1131	970	543	211	30	6650
SYRACUSE	6	28	132	415	744	1153	1271	1140	1004	570	248	45	6756
N.C. ASHEVILLE	0	0	48	245	555	775	784	683	592	273	87	0	4042
CAPE HATTERAS	0	0	0	78	273	521	580	518	440	177	25	0	2612
CHARLOTTE	0	0	6	124	438	691	691	582	481	156	22	0	3191
GREENSBORO	0	0	33	192	513	778	784	672	552	234	47	0	3805
RALEIGH	0	0	21	164	450	716	725	616	487	180	34	0	3393
WILMINGTON	0	0	0	74	291	521	546	462	357	96	0	0	2347
WINSTON SALEM	0	0	21	171	483	747	753	652	524	207	37	0	3595
N. DAK. BISMARCK	34	28	222	577	1083	1463	1708	1442	1203	645	329	117	8851
DEVILS LAKE	40	53	273	642	1191	1634	1872	1579	1345	753	381	138	9901
FARGO	28	37	219	574	1107	1569	1789	1520	1262	690	332	99	9226
WILLISTON	31	43	261	601	1122	1513	1758	1473	1262	681	357	141	9243
OHIO AKRON	0	9	96	381	726	1070	1138	1016	871	489	202	39	6037
CINCINNATI	0	0	54	248	612	921	970	837	701	336	118	9	4806
CLEVELAND	9	25	105	384	738	1088	1159	1047	918	552	260	66	6351
COLUMBUS	0	6	84	347	714	1039	1088	949	809	426	171	27	5660
DAYTON	0	6	78	310	696	1045	1097	955	809	429	167	30	5622
MANSFIELD	9	22	114	397	768	1110	1169	1042	924	543	245	60	6403
SANDUSKY	0	6	66	313	684	1032	1107	991	868	495	198	36	5796
TOLEDO	0	16	117	406	792	1138	1200	1056	924	543	242	60	6494
YOUNGSTOWN	6	19	120	412	771	1104	1169	1047	921	540	248	60	6417
OKLA. OKLAHOMA CITY	0	0	15	164	498	766	868	664	527	189	34	0	3725
TULSA	0	0	18	158	522	787	893	683	539	213	47	0	3860
OREG. ASTORIA	146	130	210	375	561	679	753	622	636	480	363	231	5186
BURNS	12	37	210	515	867	1113	1246	988	856	570	366	177	6957
EUGENE	34	34	129	366	585	719	803	627	589	426	279	135	4726
MEACHAM	84	124	288	580	918	1091	1209	1005	983	726	527	339	7874
MEDFORD	0	0	78	372	678	871	918	697	642	432	242	78	5008
PENDLETON	0	0	111	350	711	884	1017	773	617	396	205	63	5127
PORTLAND	25	28	114	335	597	735	825	644	586	396	245	105	4635
ROSEBURG	22	16	105	329	567	713	766	608	570	405	267	123	4491
SALEM	37	31	111	338	594	729	822	647	611	417	273	144	4754
SEXTON SUMMIT	81	81	171	443	666	874	958	809	818	609	465	279	6254
PA. ALLENTOWN	0	0	90	353	693	1045	1116	1002	849	471	167	24	5810
ERIE	0	25	102	391	714	1063	1169	1081	973	585	288	60	6451
HARRISBURG	0	0	63	298	648	992	1045	907	766	396	124	12	5251
PHILADELPHIA	0	0	60	291	621	964	1014	890	744	390	115	12	5101
PITTSBURGH	0	9	105	375	726	1063	1119	1002	874	480	195	39	5987
READING	0	0	54	257	597	939	1001	885	735	372	105	0	4945
SCRANTON	0	19	132	434	762	1104	1156	1028	893	498	195	33	6254
WILLIAMSPORT	0	9	111	375	717	1073	1122	1002	856	468	177	24	5934
R. I. BLOCK IS.	0	16	78	307	594	902	1020	955	877	612	344	99	5804
PROVIDENCE	0	16	96	372	660	1023	1110	988	868	534	236	51	5954
S. C. CHARLESTON	0	0	0	59	282	471	487	389	291	54	0	0	2033
COLUMBIA	0	0	0	84	345	577	570	470	357	81	0	0	2484
FLORENCE	0	0	0	78	315	552	552	459	347	84	0	0	2387
GREENVILLE	0	0	0	112	387	636	648	535	434	120	12	0	2884
SPARTANBURG	0	0	15	130	417	667	663	560	453	144	25	0	3074
S. DAK. HURON	9	12	165	508	1014	1432	1628	1355	1125	600	288	87	8223
RAPID CITY	22	12	165	481	897	1172	1333	1145	1051	615	326	126	7345
SIOUX FALLS	19	25	168	462	972	1361	1544	1285	1082	573	270	78	7839
TENN. BRISTOL	0	0	51	236	573	828	828	700	598	261	68	0	4143
CHATTANOOGA	0	0	18	143	468	698	722	577	453	150	25	0	3254
KNOXVILLE	0	0	30	171	489	725	732	613	493	198	43	0	3494
MEMPHIS	0	0	18	130	447	698	729	585	456	147	22	0	3232
NASHVILLE	0	0	30	158	495	732	778	644	512	189	40	0	3578
OAK RIDGE (CO)	0	0	39	192	531	772	778	669	552	228	56	0	3817
TEX. ABILENE	0	0	0	99	366	586	642	470	347	114	0	0	2624
AMARILLO	0	0	18	205	570	797	877	664	546	252	56	0	3985
AUSTIN	0	0	0	31	225	388	468	325	223	51	0	0	1711
BROWNSVILLE	0	0	0	0	66	149	205	106	74	0	0	0	600
CORPUS CHRISTI	0	0	0	0	120	220	291	174	109	0	0	0	914
DALLAS	0	0	0	62	321	524	601	440	319	90	6	0	2363
EL PASO	0	0	0	84	414	648	685	445	319	105	0	0	2700
FORT WORTH	0	0	0	65	324	536	614	448	319	99	0	0	2405
GALVESTON	0	0	0	0	138	270	350	258	189	30	0	0	1235
HOUSTON	0	0	0	6	183	307	384	288	192	36	0	0	1396
LAREDO	0	0	0	0	105	217	267	134	74	0	0	0	797
LUBBOCK	0	0	18	174	513	744	800	613	484	201	31	0	3578
MIDLAND	0	0	0	87	381	592	651	468	322	90	0	0	2591
PORT ARTHUR	0	0	0	22	207	329	384	274	192	39	0	0	1447
SAN ANGELO	0	0	0	68	318	536	567	412	288	66	0	0	2255
SAN ANTONIO	0	0	0	31	207	363	428	286	195	39	0	0	1549
VICTORIA	0	0	0	6	150	270	344	230	152	21	0	0	1173
WACO	0	0	0	43	270	456	536	389	270	66	0	0	2030
WICHITA FALLS	0	0	0	99	381	632	698	518	378	120	6	0	2832
UTAH MILFORD	0	0	99	443	867	1141	1252	988	822	519	279	87	6497
SALT LAKE CITY	0	0	81	419	849	1082	1172	910	763	459	233	84	6052
WENDOVER	0	0	48	372	822	1091	1178	902	729	408	177	51	5778
VT. BURLINGTON	28	65	207	539	891	1349	1513	1333	1187	714	353	90	8269
VA. CAPE HENRY	0	0	0	112	360	645	694	633	536	246	53	0	3279
LYNCHBURG	0	0	51	223	540	822	849	731	605	267	78	0	4166
NORFOLK	0	0	0	136	408	698	738	655	533	216	37	0	3421
RICHMOND	0	0	36	214	495	784	815	703	546	219	53	0	3865
ROANOKE	0	0	51	229	549	825	834	722	614	261	65	0	4150
WASH. NAT'L. AP.	0	0	33	217	519	834	871	762	626	288	74	0	4224
WASH. OLYMPIA	68	71	198	422	636	753	834	675	645	450	307	177	5236
SEATTLE	50	47	129	329	543	657	738	599	577	396	242	117	4424
SEATTLE BOEING	34	40	147	384	624	763	831	655	608	411	242	99	4838
SEATTLE TACOMA	56	62	162	391	633	750	828	678	657	474	295	159	5145
SPOKANE	9	25	168	493	879	1082	1231	980	834	531	288	135	6655
STAMPEDE PASS	273	291	393	701	1008	1178	1287	1075	1085	855	654	483	9283
TATOOSH IS.	295	279	306	406	534	639	713	613	645	525	431	333	5719
WALLA WALLA	0	0	87	310	681	843	986	745	589	342	177	45	4805
YAKIMA	0	12	144	450	828	1039	1163	868	713	435	220	69	5941
W. VA. CHARLESTON	0	0	63	254	591	865	880	770	648	300	96	9	4476
ELKINS	9	25	135	400	729	992	1008	896	791	444	198	48	5675
HUNTINGTON	0	0	63	257	585	856	880	764	636	294	99	12	4446
PARKERSBURG	0	0	60	264	606	905	942	826	691	339	115	6	4754
WIS. GREEN BAY	28	50	174	484	924	1333	1494	1313	1141	654	335	99	8029
LA CROSSE	12	19	153	437	924	1339	1504	1277	1070	540	245	69	7589
MADISON	25	40	174	474	930	1330	1473	1274	1113	618	310	102	7863
MILWAUKEE	43	47	174	471	876	1252	1376	1193	1054	642	372	135	7635
WYO. CASPER	6	16	192	524	942	1169	1290	1084	1020	657	381	129	7410
CHEYENNE	19	31	210	543	924	1101	1228	1056	1011	672	381	102	7278
LANDER	6	19	204	555	1020	1299	1417	1145	1017	654	381	153	7870
SHERIAN	25	31	219	539	948	1200	1355	1154	1054	642	366	150	7683

MEAN PERCENTAGE OF POSSIBLE SUNSHINE FOR SELECTED LOCATIONS

STATE AND STATION	YEARS	JAN.	FEB.	MAR.	APR.	MAY	JUNE	JULY	AUG.	SEPT.	OCT.	NOV.	DEC.	ANNUAL
ALA. BIRMINGHAM	56	43	49	56	63	66	67	62	65	66	67	58	44	59
MONTGOMERY	49	51	53	61	69	73	72	66	69	69	71	64	48	64
ALASKA. ANCHORAGE	19	39	46	56	58	50	51	45	39	35	32	33	29	45
FAIRBANKS	20	34	50	61	68	55	53	45	35	31	28	38	29	44
JUNEAU	14	30	32	39	37	34	35	28	30	25	18	21	18	30
NOME	29	44	46	48	53	51	48	32	26	34	35	36	30	41
ARIZ. PHOENIX	64	76	79	83	88	93	94	84	84	89	88	84	77	85
YUMA	52	83	87	91	94	97	98	92	91	93	93	90	83	91
ARK. LITTLE ROCK	66	44	53	57	62	67	72	71	73	71	74	58	47	62
CALIF. EUREKA	49	40	44	50	53	54	56	51	46	52	48	42	39	49
FRESNO	55	46	63	72	83	89	94	97	97	93	87	73	47	78
LOS ANGELES	63	70	69	70	67	68	69	80	81	80	76	79	72	73
RED BLUFF	39	50	60	65	75	79	86	95	94	89	77	64	50	75
SACRAMENTO	48	44	57	67	76	82	90	96	95	92	82	65	44	77
SAN DIEGO	68	68	67	68	66	60	60	67	70	70	70	76	71	68
SAN FRANCISCO	64	53	57	63	69	70	75	68	63	70	70	62	54	66
COLO. DENVER	64	67	67	65	63	61	69	68	68	71	71	67	65	67
GRAND JUNCTION	57	58	62	64	67	71	79	79	77	74	67	58	49	69
CONN. HARTFORD	48	46	55	56	54	57	60	62	60	57	55	46	46	56
D. C. WASHINGTON	66	46	53	56	57	61	64	64	62	62	61	54	47	58
FLA. APALACHICOLA	26	59	62	62	71	77	70	64	63	62	74	66	53	65
JACKSONVILLE	60	58	59	66	71	71	63	62	63	58	58	61	53	62
KEY WEST	45	68	75	78	78	76	70	69	71	65	65	69	66	71
MIAMI BEACH	48	66	72	73	73	68	62	65	67	62	62	65	65	67
TAMPA	63	63	67	71	74	75	66	61	64	64	67	67	61	68
GA. ATLANTA	65	48	53	57	65	68	68	62	63	65	67	60	47	60
HAWAII. HILO	9	48	42	41	34	31	41	44	38	42	41	49	48	
HONOLULU	53	62	64	60	62	64	66	67	70	70	68	63	60	65
LIHUE	9	48	48	48	46	51	60	58	59	67	58	51	49	54
IDAHO. BOISE	20	40	48	59	67	68	75	89	86	81	66	46	37	66
POCATELLO	21	37	47	58	64	66	72	82	81	78	66	48	36	64
ILL. CAIRO	30	46	53	59	65	71	77	82	79	75	73	64	48	60
CHICAGO	66	44	49	53	56	63	69	73	70	65	61	47	41	59
SPRINGFIELD	59	47	51	54	58	64	69	76	72	73	64	53	45	60
IND. EVANSVILLE	48	42	49	55	61	67	73	78	76	73	67	52	42	64
FT. WAYNE	48	38	44	51	55	62	69	74	69	64	58	41	38	57
INDIANAPOLIS	63	41	47	49	55	62	68	74	70	68	64	48	39	57
IOWA. DES MOINES	66	56	56	56	59	62	66	75	70	64	64	53	48	62
DUBUQUE	54	48	52	52	58	60	63	73	67	61	61	46	40	57
SIOUX CITY	52	55	58	58	59	63	67	75	72	67	65	53	50	63
KANS. CONCORDIA	52	60	60	62	63	65	73	79	76	72	70	64	58	67
DODGE CITY	70	67	66	68	68	68	74	78	78	76	75	70	67	71
WICHITA	46	61	63	64	64	66	73	80	77	73	68	64	58	69
KY. LOUISVILLE	59	41	47	52	57	64	68	72	69	68	64	51	39	59
LA. NEW ORLEANS	69	49	50	57	63	66	64	58	60	64	70	60	46	59
SHREVEPORT	18	48	54	58	60	69	78	79	80	79	77	65	60	69
MAINE. EASTPORT	58	45	51	52	52	51	53	55	57	54	50	37	40	50
MASS. BOSTON	67	47	56	57	56	59	64	69	64	61	54	47	48	57
MICH. ALPENA	45	29	43	52	56	59	64	70	64	52	44	24	22	51
DETROIT	69	34	42	48	52	58	65	69	66	61	54	37	34	52
GRAND RAPIDS	56	26	37	48	54	60	66	72	67	58	50	31	22	49
MARQUETTE	55	31	40	47	52	53	56	63	57	47	38	24	24	47
S. STE. MARIE	60	28	44	50	54	54	59	63	58	47	36	21	22	47
MINN. DULUTH	49	47	55	60	58	58	60	68	63	53	47	36	40	55
MINNEAPOLIS	45	49	54	55	57	60	64	72	69	60	54	40	40	56
MISS. VICKSBURG	66	46	50	57	64	69	73	69	72	74	71	60	45	64
MO. KANSAS CITY	69	55	57	59	60	64	70	76	72	70	67	59	52	65
ST. LOUIS	68	48	49	56	59	64	68	72	68	67	65	54	44	61
SPRINGFIELD	45	48	54	57	60	63	69	77	72	71	65	58	48	63
MONT. HAVRE	55	49	58	61	63	63	65	78	75	64	57	48	46	62
HELENA	65	46	55	58	60	59	63	77	74	63	57	48	43	60
KALISPELL	50	28	40	49	57	58	60	77	73	61	50	28	20	53
NEBR. LINCOLN	55	57	59	60	60	63	69	76	71	67	66	59	55	64
NORTH PLATTE	53	63	63	64	62	64	72	78	74	72	70	62	58	68
NEV. ELY	21	61	64	68	65	67	79	79	81	81	73	67	62	72
LAS VEGAS	19	74	77	78	81	85	91	84	86	92	84	83	75	82
RENO	51	59	64	69	75	77	82	90	89	86	76	68	56	76
WINNEMUCCA	53	52	60	64	70	76	83	90	90	86	75	62	53	74
N. H. CONCORD	44	48	53	55	53	51	56	57	58	55	50	43	43	52
N. J. ATLANTIC CITY	62	51	57	58	59	62	65	67	66	65	54	58	52	60
N. MEX. ALBUQUERQUE	28	70	72	72	76	79	84	76	75	81	80	79	70	78
ROSWELL	47	69	72	75	77	76	80	76	75	74	74	74	69	74
N. Y. ALBANY	63	43	51	53	53	57	62	63	61	58	54	39	38	53
BINGHAMTON	63	31	39	41	44	50	56	54	51	47	43	29	26	44
BUFFALO	49	32	41	49	51	59	67	70	67	60	51	31	28	53
CANTON	43	37	47	50	48	54	61	63	61	54	45	30	31	49
NEW YORK	83	49	56	57	59	62	65	66	64	64	61	53	50	59
SYRACUSE	49	31	38	45	50	58	64	67	63	56	47	29	26	50
N. C. ASHEVILLE	57	48	53	56	61	64	63	59	59	62	63	64	52	58
RALEIGH	61	50	56	59	64	67	65	62	62	63	64	62	52	61
N. DAK. BISMARCK	65	52	58	56	57	58	61	73	69	62	59	49	48	59
DEVILS LAKE	55	53	60	59	60	59	62	71	67	59	56	44	45	58
FARGO	39	47	55	56	58	62	63	73	69	60	57	39	46	59
WILLISTON	43	51	59	60	63	66	66	78	75	63	60	48	48	60
OHIO. CINCINNATI	44	41	46	52	56	62	69	72	68	68	60	46	39	57
CLEVELAND	65	29	36	45	52	61	67	71	68	64	56	43	31	53
COLUMBUS	65	36	44	49	54	63	68	71	68	66	60	44	35	55
OKLA. OKLAHOMA CITY	62	57	60	63	64	65	74	78	78	74	68	64	57	68
OREG. BAKER	46	41	49	56	61	63	67	83	81	74	62	46	37	60
PORTLAND	69	27	34	41	49	52	55	70	65	55	42	28	23	48
ROSEBURG	29	24	32	40	51	57	64	70	65	55	42	28	23	46
PA. HARRISBURG	60	43	52	55	57	61	65	68	63	62	58	47	43	57
PHILADELPHIA	66	45	56	57	58	61	62	64	61	62	61	53	49	57
PITTSBURGH	63	32	39	45	50	57	62	64	60	61	54	39	30	51
R. I. BLOCK ISLAND	48	45	54	47	56	58	60	62	62	60	59	50	44	56
S. C. CHARLESTON	61	58	60	65	72	73	70	66	66	67	68	68	57	66
COLUMBIA	55	53	57	62	68	69	68	63	65	64	68	64	51	63
S. DAK. HURON	62	55	62	63	62	61	66	78	72	66	61	54	52	63
RAPID CITY	53	58	62	63	62	61	66	73	73	69	66	58	54	64
TENN. KNOXVILLE	62	42	49	53	59	64	66	64	66	64	59	54	41	57
MEMPHIS	55	44	51	57	64	68	74	73	74	70	69	58	45	64
NASHVILLE	63	42	47	54	60	65	69	69	68	69	65	53	42	59
TEX. ABILENE	14	64	68	73	76	73	86	83	85	73	71	72	66	73
AMARILLO	54	71	71	75	75	75	82	81	81	79	76	76	70	76
AUSTIN	33	46	50	57	60	66	74	78	78	74	67	56	49	62
BROWNSVILLE	37	44	49	51	57	65	73	78	78	67	70	54	44	61
DEL RIO	36	53	55	61	63	66	73	80	80	69	68	58	52	63
EL PASO	53	74	77	81	85	87	87	78	78	80	82	80	73	80
FT. WORTH	33	56	57	61	63	66	75	78	78	74	72	60	48	63
GALVESTON	66	50	50	55	61	69	76	72	71	70	74	62	49	63
SAN ANTONIO	57	48	51	56	58	60	69	74	75	69	67	55	49	62
UTAH. SALT LAKE CITY	22	48	53	61	67	73	78	82	82	84	73	59	48	68
VT. BURLINGTON	54	34	43	48	47	53	60	62	59	51	43	25	24	46
VA. NORFOLK	60	50	57	60	63	67	66	65	62	63	64	60	51	61
RICHMOND	56	49	55	59	63	67	66	65	62	63	64	58	50	61
WASH. NORTH HEAD	44	28	37	42	48	48	50	46	48	43	31	27	24	41
SEATTLE	26	27	34	42	48	53	48	62	56	53	36	28	24	45
SPOKANE	62	26	41	53	63	64	68	82	79	68	53	28	22	58
TATOOSH ISLAND	49	26	36	43	47	48	47	44	47	38	26	23	24	44
WALLA WALLA	44	24	35	51	63	67	72	86	84	72	59	33	20	60
YAKIMA	18	34	49	62	70	72	74	86	86	74	61	33	26	59
W. VA. ELKINS	55	33	37	42	47	55	55	56	53	55	51	41	33	48
PARKERSBURG	62	30	36	42	49	56	60	63	60	60	53	37	29	48
WIS. GREEN BAY	57	44	51	55	56	59	64	70	65	58	52	40	40	55
MADISON	59	44	49	52	53	58	64	70	66	60	56	41	38	56
MILWAUKEE	59	44	48	53	56	60	65	73	67	62	56	44	39	57
WYO. CHEYENNE	63	65	66	64	61	59	68	70	68	69	69	65	63	66
LANDER	57	66	70	71	66	65	67	76	75	67	60	53	52	64
SHERIDAN	52	56	61	62	61	61	67	76	74	67	60	53	52	64
YELLOWSTONE PARK	35	39	51	55	57	56	63	73	71	65	57	45	38	56
P. R. SAN JUAN	57	64	69	71	66	59	62	65	67	61	63	63	65	65

Based on period of record through December 1959, except in a few instances.

MEAN NUMBER OF HOURS OF SUNSHINE

STATE AND STATION	YEARS	JAN.	FEB.	MAR.	APR.	MAY	JUNE	JULY	AUG.	SEPT.	OCT.	NOV.	DEC.	ANNUAL
ALA. BIRMINGHAM	30	138	152	207	248	293	294	269	265	244	234	182	136	2662
MOBILE	22	157	158	212	253	301	289	249	259	235	254	195	146	2708
MONTGOMERY	30	160	168	227	267	317	311	288	290	260	250	200	156	2894
ALASKA ANCHORAGE	19	78	114	210	254	268	288	255	184	128	96	68	49	1992
FAIRBANKS	20	54	120	224	302	319	334	274	164	122	85	71	36	2105
JUNEAU	29	71	102	171	200	230	251	193	161	123	67	60	51	1680
NOME	27	72	109	193	226	285	297	204	146	142	101	67	42	1884
ARIZ. PHOENIX	30	248	244	314	346	404	404	377	351	334	307	267	236	3832
PRESCOTT	14	222	230	293	323	378	392	323	305	315	286	254	228	3549
TUCSON	13	255	266	317	350	399	394	329	329	335	317	280	258	3829
YUMA	30	258	266	337	365	419	420	404	380	351	330	285	262	4077
ARK. FT. SMITH	30	146	156	202	234	268	303	321	305	261	230	174	147	2747
LITTLE ROCK	30	143	158	213	243	291	316	321	316	265	251	181	142	2840
CALIF. EUREKA	30	120	138	180	209	247	261	244	205	195	164	127	108	2198
FRESNO	29	153	192	283	330	389	418	435	406	355	306	221	144	3632
LOS ANGELES	30	224	217	273	264	292	299	352	336	295	263	249	220	3284
RED BLUFF	15	156	186	246	302	366	396	438	407	341	277	199	154	3468
SACRAMENTO	30	134	169	255	300	367	405	437	406	347	283	197	122	3422
SAN DIEGO	30	216	212	262	242	261	253	293	277	255	234	236	217	2958
SAN FRANCISCO	30	165	182	251	281	314	330	300	272	267	243	198	156	2959
COLO. DENVER	30	207	205	247	252	281	311	321	297	274	246	200	192	3033
GRAND JUNCTION	30	169	182	243	265	314	350	349	311	291	255	198	168	3095
PUEBLO	30	224	217	261	271	299	340	349	318	290	265	225	211	3270
CONN. HARTFORD	30	141	166	206	223	267	285	299	268	220	193	137	136	2541
NEW HAVEN	30	155	178	215	234	274	291	309	284	238	215	157	154	2704
D. C. WASHINGTON	30	138	160	205	226	267	288	291	264	233	207	162	135	2576
FLA. APALACHICOLA	26	193	195	233	274	328	296	273	259	236	263	216	175	2941
JACKSONVILLE	30	192	189	241	267	296	260	255	248	199	205	191	170	2713
KEY WEST	30	229	238	285	296	307	273	277	269	236	237	226	225	3098
LAKELAND	7	204	186	222	251	285	268	252	242	203	209	212	198	2732
MIAMI	30	222	227	266	275	280	251	267	263	216	215	212	209	2903
PENSACOLA	30	175	180	232	270	311	302	278	284	249	265	206	166	2918
TAMPA	30	223	220	260	283	320	275	257	252	232	243	227	209	3001
GA. ATLANTA	25	154	165	218	266	309	304	284	285	247	241	188	160	2821
MACON	30	177	178	235	279	321	314	292	295	253	236	202	168	2950
SAVANNAH	30	175	173	229	274	307	279	267	256	212	216	197	167	2752
HAWAII HILO	7	153	135	161	112	106	158	184	134	137	153	106	131	1670
HONOLULU	30	227	202	250	255	276	280	293	290	279	257	221	211	3041
LIHUE	10	171	162	176	176	211	246	246	236	246	210	170	161	2411
IDAHO BOISE	30	116	144	218	274	322	352	412	378	311	232	143	104	3006
POCATELLO	30	111	143	211	255	300	338	380	347	296	230	145	108	2864
ILL. CAIRO	15	124	160	218	254	298	324	345	336	279	254	181	145	2918
CHICAGO	30	126	142	199	221	274	300	333	299	247	216	136	118	2611
MOLINE	18	132	139	189	214	255	279	337	300	251	214	130	123	2563
PEORIA	30	134	149	198	229	273	303	336	299	259	222	149	122	2673
SPRINGFIELD	30	127	149	193	224	282	304	346	312	266	225	152	122	2702
IND. EVANSVILLE	30	123	145	199	237	294	322	342	318	274	236	156	120	2766
FT. WAYNE	30	113	136	191	217	281	310	342	306	242	210	120	102	2570
INDIANAPOLIS	30	118	140	193	227	278	313	342	313	265	222	139	118	2668
TERRE HAUTE	24	125	148	189	231	274	302	341	305	253	235	150	122	2675
IOWA BURLINGTON	19	148	165	217	241	284	315	353	327	270	243	175	147	2885
CHARLES CITY	22	137	157	190	226	258	285	336	290	241	207	130	115	2572
DES MOINES	30	155	170	203	236	276	303	346	299	263	227	156	136	2770
SIOUX CITY	30	164	177	216	254	300	320	363	320	270	236	160	146	2926
KAN. CONCORDIA	30	180	172	214	243	281	315	348	308	249	245	189	172	2916
DODGE CITY	30	205	191	249	268	305	335	359	335	290	266	218	198	3219
TOPEKA	18	159	160	193	215	260	287	310	304	263	229	173	149	2702
WICHITA	30	187	186	233	254	291	321	350	325	277	245	206	182	3057
KY. LOUISVILLE	30	115	135	188	221	283	303	324	295	256	219	148	114	2601
LA. NEW ORLEANS	30	160	158	213	247	292	287	260	269	241	260	200	157	2744
SHREVEPORT	19	151	172	214	240	298	332	339	322	289	273	208	177	3015
MAINE EASTPORT	22	133	151	196	201	245	248	275	260	205	175	105	115	2309
PORTLAND	30	155	174	213	226	268	286	312	294	229	202	146	148	2653
MD. BALTIMORE	30	148	170	211	229	270	295	299	272	238	212	164	145	2653
MASS. BLUE HILL OBS.	10	125	136	165	182	233	248	266	241	211	181	134	135	2257
BOSTON	30	148	168	212	222	263	283	300	280	232	207	152	148	2615
NANTUCKET	22	128	156	214	227	278	284	291	279	242	208	149	129	2585
MICH. ALPENA	24	86	124	198	228	261	303	339	285	204	159	70	67	2324
DETROIT	30	90	128	180	212	263	295	321	284	226	189	98	89	2375
LANSING	30	84	119	175	215	272	305	344	294	228	182	87	73	2378
ESCANABA	30	112	148	204	226	266	283	316	267	198	162	90	94	2366
GRAND RAPIDS	30	74	117	178	218	277	308	349	304	231	188	92	70	2406
MARQUETTE	30	78	113	172	207	248	268	305	251	186	142	68	66	2104
SAULT STE. MARIE	30	83	123	187	217	252	269	309	256	165	133	61	62	2117
MINN. DULUTH	30	125	163	221	235	268	282	328	277	203	166	100	107	2475
MINNEAPOLIS	30	140	166	200	231	272	302	343	296	237	193	115	112	2607
MISS. JACKSON	12	130	147	199	244	280	287	279	287	235	223	185	150	2646
VICKSBURG	30	136	141	199	232	284	304	291	297	254	244	183	140	2705
MO. COLUMBIA	30	147	164	207	232	281	296	341	298	262	225	166	138	2757
KANSAS CITY	30	154	170	211	235	278	313	347	308	266	235	178	151	2846
ST. JOSEPH	23	154	165	211	231	274	301	347	287	260	224	168	144	2766
ST. LOUIS	30	137	152	202	235	283	301	325	289	256	223	166	125	2694
SPRINGFIELD	30	145	164	213	238	278	305	342	310	269	233	183	140	2820
MONT. BILLINGS	21	140	154	208	236	283	301	372	332	258	213	136	129	2762
GREAT FALLS	19	154	176	245	261	299	299	381	342	256	206	132	133	2884
HAVRE	30	136	174	234	268	311	312	384	339	260	202	132	122	2874
HELENA	30	138	168	215	241	292	292	342	336	258	202	137	121	2742
MISSOULA	25	85	109	167	209	261	260	378	328	246	178	90	66	2377
NEBR. LINCOLN	30	173	172	213	244	287	316	356	309	266	237	174	160	2907
NORTH PLATTE	30	181	179	221	246	282	310	343	304	264	242	184	169	2925
OMAHA	30	172	188	222	259	305	332	379	311	270	248	166	145	2997
VALENTINE	30	185	194	229	252	296	323	369	326	275	242	174	172	3037
NEV. ELY	22	186	197	262	260	300	354	359	344	303	255	204	187	3211
LAS VEGAS	8	239	251	314	336	386	411	383	364	345	301	258	250	3838
RENO	30	185	199	267	306	354	376	414	391	336	273	212	170	3483
WINNEMUCCA	30	142	155	207	255	312	346	395	375	316	242	177	139	3061
N. H. CONCORD	23	136	153	192	196	229	261	286	260	214	179	122	126	2354
MT. WASHINGTON OBS.	18	94	98	133	141	162	145	150	143	139	159	89	87	1540
N. J. ATLANTIC CITY	30	151	173	210	233	273	287	298	271	239	218	177	153	2683
TRENTON	30	145	168	203	235	277	294	309	273	239	208	160	142	2653
N. MEX. ALBUQUERQUE	30	221	218	273	299	343	365	340	317	299	279	245	219	3418
ROSWELL	21	218	223	286	306	330	333	341	313	266	266	242	216	3340
N. Y. ALBANY	30	125	151	194	213	266	301	317	286	224	192	115	112	2496
BINGHAMTON	30	94	119	151	170	226	256	266	230	184	158	92	79	2025
BUFFALO	30	110	125	180	212	274	319	338	297	239	183	97	84	2458
NEW YORK	30	154	171	213	237	268	289	302	271	235	213	169	155	2677
ROCHESTER	30	93	123	172	209	274	314	333	294	224	173	97	86	2392
SYRACUSE	30	87	115	165	197	261	295	316	276	211	163	81	74	2241
N. C. ASHEVILLE	30	146	161	211	247	289	292	268	250	235	222	179	146	2646
CAPE HATTERAS	9	152	168	206	259	293	301	286	265	214	202	169	154	2669
CHARLOTTE	30	165	177	230	267	313	316	291	277	247	243	198	167	2891
GREENSBORO	30	157	171	217	231	298	302	287	272	243	236	190	163	2767
RALEIGH	29	154	168	220	255	290	284	277	253	224	215	184	156	2680
WILMINGTON	30	179	180	237	279	314	312	286	273	237	238	206	178	2919
N. DAK. BISMARCK	30	141	170	205	236	279	294	358	307	243	198	130	125	2686
DEVILS LAKE	30	150	177	220	250	291	297	352	302	230	198	123	124	2714
FARGO	30	132	170	210	232	283	288	343	293	222	187	112	114	2586
WILLISTON	29	141	168	215	260	305	312	377	328	247	206	131	129	2819
OHIO CINCINNATI (ABBE)	30	115	137	186	222	273	309	323	295	253	205	138	118	2574
CLEVELAND	30	79	111	167	209	274	301	325	288	235	187	99	77	2352
COLUMBUS	30	112	132	177	215	270	296	323	291	250	210	131	101	2508
DAYTON	10	114	136	195	222	281	313	323	307	268	229	152	124	2664
SANDUSKY	30	100	128	183	229	285	312	343	302	248	201	111	91	2533
TOLEDO	30	93	120	170	203	263	296	331	298	241	196	106	92	2409
OKLA. OKLAHOMA CITY	29	175	182	235	253	290	329	352	331	282	243	201	175	3048
TULSA	18	152	164	200	213	244	287	314	308	281	241	207	172	2783
OREG. BAKER	22	118	143	198	251	302	313	406	368	289	215	132	100	2835
PORTLAND	30	77	97	142	203	246	249	329	275	218	134	87	65	2122
ROSEBURG	30	69	96	148	205	257	278	369	329	255	146	81	50	2283
PA. HARRISBURG	30	132	160	203	230	277	297	319	282	233	200	140	131	2604
PHILADELPHIA	30	142	166	203	231	270	281	288	253	225	205	158	142	2564
PITTSBURGH	25	89	114	163	200	239	260	283	250	234	180	114	76	2202
READING	30	133	151	195	220	259	275	293	259	219	198	144	127	2473
SCRANTON	30	108	138	178	199	251	269	290	249	213	183	120	105	2303
R. I. PROVIDENCE	30	145	168	211	221	271	285	292	267	226	207	153	143	2589
S. C. CHARLESTON	30	188	189	243	284	323	308	297	281	244	239	210	187	2993
COLUMBIA	30	173	183	233	274	312	312	291	283	243	242	202	166	2914
GREENVILLE	26	166	176	227	274	307	300	278	274	239	232	192	157	2822
S. DAK. HURON	30	153	177	213	250	295	321	367	320	260	212	142	134	2844
RAPID CITY	30	164	182	222	245	278	300	348	317	266	228	164	144	2858
TENN. CHATTANOOGA	30	126	146	187	239	290	295	278	266	247	220	169	128	2591
KNOXVILLE	30	124	144	189	237	281	288	277	248	237	213	157	120	2515
MEMPHIS	30	135	152	204	244	296	321	319	314	261	243	180	139	2808
NASHVILLE	30	123	142	196	241	285	308	292	279	250	224	168	126	2634
TEX. ABILENE	13	190	199	250	259	290	347	335	322	276	245	223	201	3137
AMARILLO	30	207	199	258	276	305	338	350	328	288	260	229	205	3243
AUSTIN	30	148	152	207	221	266	302	331	320	261	242	180	160	2790
BROWNSVILLE	30	147	152	187	210	272	297	326	311	246	252	165	151	2716
CORPUS CHRISTI	24	160	165	212	237	295	329	366	341	276	264	194	164	3003
DALLAS	30	155	159	220	238	279	326	341	325	274	240	191	163	2911
DEL RIO	27	173	173	230	237	259	279	331	319	252	240	195	178	2866
EL PASO	30	234	236	299	329	373	369	336	327	300	287	257	236	3583
GALVESTON	30	151	149	203	230	288	322	305	292	257	264	199	151	2811
HOUSTON	30	144	141	193	212	266	298	294	281	238	239	181	146	2633
PORT ARTHUR	30	153	149	209	235	292	317	285	281	252	256	191	148	2768
SAN ANTONIO	30	148	153	213	224	258	292	325	307	261	241	183	160	2765
UTAH SALT LAKE CITY	30	137	155	227	269	329	358	377	346	306	249	171	135	3059
VT. BURLINGTON	30	103	127	184	185	244	270	291	266	199	152	77	80	2178
VA. LYNCHBURG	26	153	169	216	243	288	297	288	264	235	217	177	158	2705
NORFOLK	30	156	174	223	257	304	311	296	282	237	220	182	161	2803
RICHMOND	30	144	166	211	248	280	296	286	263	230	211	176	152	2663
WASH. NORTH HEAD	22	76	97	135	182	221	214	226	186	170	123	87	66	1783
SEATTLE	30	74	99	154	201	247	234	304	248	197	122	77	62	2019
SPOKANE	30	78	120	197	262	308	309	397	350	264	177	86	57	2605
TATOOSH ISLAND	30	70	100	135	182	229	217	235	190	175	129	71	60	1793
WALLA WALLA	30	72	106	194	262	317	335	411	367	280	198	92	51	2685
W. VA. ELKINS	24	110	119	158	198	227	256	225	236	211	186	131	103	2160
PARKERSBURG	30	91	111	155	200	252	277	286	264	230	189	117	93	2265
WIS. GREEN BAY	30	121	148	194	210	251	279	314	266	213	176	110	106	2388
MADISON	30	126	147	196	214	258	285	336	288	230	198	116	108	2502
MILWAUKEE	30	116	134	191	218	267	293	340	292	235	193	125	106	2510
WYO. CHEYENNE	30	191	197	243	237	259	304	318	286	265	242	188	170	2900
LANDER	30	200	208	260	264	301	340	361	326	280	233	186	185	3144
SHERIDAN	30	160	179	226	245	286	303	367	333	266	221	153	145	2884
P. R. SAN JUAN	30	231	229	273	252	240	245	264	257	219	229	217	222	2878

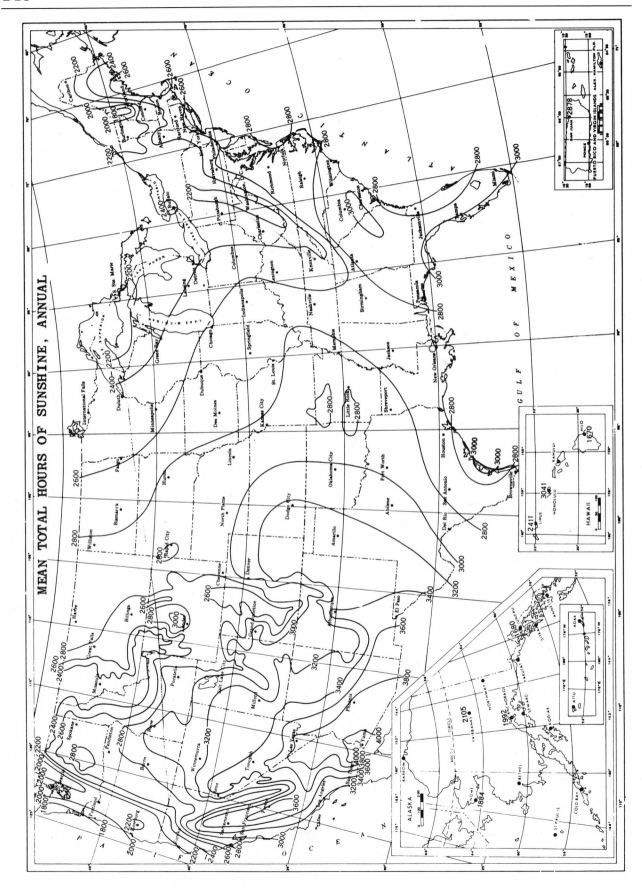

MEAN TOTAL HOURS OF SUNSHINE, ANNUAL

Appendix B: Guidelines for Passive Solar Design

As you plan your retrofit, you will need specific information on locating, sizing, and adapting solar collection surfaces, thermal storage mass, and ventilation and heat distribution openings. The following pages, along with the references provided, should provide all the data you need.

REFERENCES

Balcomb, J. D., et al. *Passive Solar Design Analysis*. Passive Solar Design Handbook, vol. 2. Washington, DC: U.S. Department of Energy, 1980.

Hawkweed Group. *Passive Solar House Book*. Chicago: Rand McNally & Co., 1980.

Mazria, Edward. *The Passive Solar Energy Book*. Emmaus, PA: Rodale Press, 1979.

Niles, Philip and Haggard, Kenneth L. *Passive Solar Handbook*. Sacramento, CA: California Energy Commission, 1980.

Total Environmental Action, Inc. *The Thermal Mass Pattern Book*. Harrisville, NH: Total Environmental Action, Inc., 1980.

SOLAR COLLECTION SURFACES

LOCATE COLLECTION SURFACES WHERE THEY

- face within 30° of true south.
- receive direct sunlight between 9:00 A.M. and 3:00 P.M. during the heating season.

- receive the greatest amount of natural shading during the cooling season or where a trellis, movable louvers, awnings, roof overhangs, decks, lofts, or other external or internal shading devices can be used.
- can collect diffuse sky radiation, especially in cloudy climates (i.e., locate some collector surfaces in south-sloping roof areas of house, greenhouse, or sunspace).
- allow the sun to strike existing or newly placed thermal storage mass (or absorber surfaces) during the heating season only.

Note: It may be desirable to "collect" light from other directions, especially north, to balance the sunlight collected from the south and prevent glare. Window openings to the north, east and west should be comparatively smaller than those for the south, and their combined total area should be at least 10 percent of the area of south-facing glazing.

SIZE COLLECTION SURFACES

- as a general rule of thumb, the south-facing glazing in rooms you want to heat by direct solar gain should total about 13 percent of the floor area for those rooms; e.g., to heat a 1,000-square-foot (92.9-ca) living area, use approximately 130 square feet (12.1 ca) of south-facing glazing. In extremely cold climates, over 7,500 DD/yr., south-facing glazing should total about 15 percent of the floor area; in warmer climates (less than 4,500 DD/yr.), south-facing glazing should total about 10 percent of the floor area.
- use standard-size windows, sliding glass doors, skylights, and roof windows for direct solar gain to interior space. (Standard sizes are less expensive.)
- use readily available standard sizes—28 by 76 inches (71.1 × 193 cm), 34 by 76 inches (86.4 × 193 cm), or 46 by 76 inches (124.4 × 193 cm)—of patio door replacement units (double insulated, tempered glass) for sun-

spaces, solar porches, waterwalls, Trombe walls, TAPs, or window box heaters. (This is usually the least expensive double insulated glass you can buy.)
- avoid collecting more heat than you can use (or store for later use) or more heat than you want in late spring, summer, and early fall. (See sizing procedures for thermal storage mass in next section.)
- use acrylic or fiberglass glazing materials in standard sizes—4 by 8, 10, or 12 feet (1.2 × 2.4, 3, or 3.7 m)—or rolls for greenhouses or other applications where clear glass is unnecessary; also use these materials for sunspaces, solar porches, or other collection surfaces where privacy is desirable.
- greenhouses and sunspaces should have a *glazing area* 20 to 30 percent as large as the *floor area* of the rooms of the house to be heated.
- attached solar greenhouses and sunspaces should be 8 to 10 feet (2.4 to 3 m) wide and a minimum of 12 to 16 feet (3.7 to 5.8 m) in length. As a general guideline, the area of south glazing of a greenhouse or sunspace should be about twice as large as its floor area. (Solar porches and integrated sunspaces—those built into the existing structure of the house—can follow whatever configuration is demanded by the shape of the space being enclosed, but provisions must be made to ventilate and to thermally isolate these spaces from the rest of the house through doors, windows, insulated shutters, etc.)
- window box heaters, TAPs, Trombe walls, and waterwalls should be sized to fit the space available for them and to use standard-size glazing material. (Ideally, a Trombe wall should have a surface area about one-third to three-quarters as large as the floor area of adjoining living space for which it is to provide heat—Trombe walls in cold climates should be larger; in warm climates, smaller. The surface area of a waterwall should be one-quarter to three-eighths as large as the floor area of the living space to be heated.)

ADAPT COLLECTION SURFACES

■ *increase* size of solar collection surfaces to compensate for shading of the collector area by trees or other obstructions *or* to compensate for an orientation more than 20° from true south.

■ if feasible, tilt collector surface at an angle perpendicular to the altitude of the sun at noon on December 21. For example, at 36° north latitude, the sun is about 30° above the horizon at noon on December 21st; therefore, the optimum angle for the collection surface at that latitude would be 60° from horizontal (90° − 30° = 60°).

■ greenhouse or sunspace glazing should be tilted at an angle of 25° + latitude. (For example, at 40° north latitude, glazing should be 65° from horizontal: 25° + 40° = 65°.)

■ at any latitude, but especially in the higher latitudes (40° to 48°N), vertical collector surfaces can be used without significant reduction of efficiency—especially where snow covers the ground frequently during the winter.

■ in areas where heating is required in late spring and early fall, for optimum performance tilt collector surface at an angle equal to latitude plus 10° to 15°. For example, at 45° north latitude, the tilt would be 55° to 60°.

■ in areas with a short heating season and a long cooling season, use only vertical collector surfaces. (Vertical glazing is easier to shade than tilted glazing.)

■ use translucent glazing materials in roof of house, greenhouse, or sunspace to reduce glare, aid plant growth, and scatter light and heat energy.

■ where feasible, use reflective surface to direct sunlight into collector areas and/or to thermal storage mass. Bottom-hinged exterior insulating shutter with reflective surface facing into the house, for example, will, when opened during the day, bounce sunlight into collector area.

■ use single-glazed windows and/or sliding glass doors between the house and attached greenhouses, sunspaces, solar porches, or Trombe walls if direct solar gain through these windows and doors is desired.

■ consider using triple-glazed window and door units on north-, east-, and west-facing openings.

THERMAL STORAGE MASS

LOCATE THERMAL STORAGE MASS

■ where it will be in direct (or reflected) sunlight for a major portion of the day between 9:00 A.M. and 3:00 P.M. during the heating season.

■ where it can conduct and reradiate its stored energy to living spaces.

■ where it does not receive direct sunlight during the cooling season.

■ where cooler nighttime breezes can pass over it during the cooling season.

■ where it is in thermal contact with the ground but has a vapor barrier and is insulated down to the frost line around its perimeter.

Note: If you are planning an attached greenhouse, sunspace, Trombe wall, or solar addition that covers only part of an existing masonry wall—and you want the wall to store heat—insulate the remainder of the wall on the *outside* or set up a "thermal break" between the enclosed and unenclosed portions of the wall. This will prevent the heat collected in the glass-enclosed portion from being wicked by conduction and therefore lost to the unenclosed part of the wall. Some direct solar gain on an interior freestanding masonry fireplace wall will also be wicked out through the roof if there is no thermal break between the interior and exterior masonry surfaces.

SIZE THERMAL STORAGE MASS

Masonry

■ use a ratio of 2 to 1 between the area of interior 8-inch-thick (20.3-cm) solid masonry materials (in direct sunlight) and the area of south-facing glazing, i.e., 2 square feet (.19 ca) of 8-inch (20.3-cm) masonry for each square foot (.09 ca) of south-facing glazing.

■ use a ratio of 4 to 1 between the area of interior 4-inch-thick (10.2-cm) solid masonry materials (in direct sunlight) and the area of south-facing glazing, i.e., 4 square feet (.37 ca) of 4-inch (10.2-cm) masonry for each square foot (.09 ca) of south-facing glazing.

■ use a ratio of 8 to 1 between area of interior 4-inch-thick (10.2-cm) solid masonry material (if the material is in *indirect* or *diffuse* sunlight) and area of south-facing glazing, i.e., 8 square feet (.74 ca) of 4-inch (10.2-cm) masonry for each square foot (.09 ca) of south-facing glazing.

Water

■ use 6 to 9 gallons (22.7 to 34.1 l) of water in dark-colored containers in direct sunlight (during heating season only) for each square foot (.09 ca) of south-facing glazing.

PCM

■ use 1 to 1½ gallons (3.8 to 5.7 l) of phase change materials in containers in direct sunlight (during the heating season only) for each square foot (.09 ca) of south-facing glazing.

Rock Beds

■ use 1 cubic foot (.03 s) of washed river rock (rounded, 1½ to 2 inches [3.8 to 5 cm] in diameter) for each 2 square feet (.19 ca) of solar collector surface that supplies heat to the rock storage bed.

ADAPT THERMAL STORAGE MASS

■ consider adding mass to the interior of your house by replacing an existing stud-frame wall, or by facing it with masonry materials such as 4-inch (10.2-cm) solid concrete block or brick (*consider this only if there is adequate footing to support the new masonry wall*—a concrete slab floor, for example—or where such a footing could be built).

■ use corrugated-face or other rough-textured concrete block for building new thermal storage walls. (These have more surface area than smooth-faced materials.) If such walls are built next to existing masonry walls—to produce a 12-inch-thick (30.5-cm) Trombe wall, for example—no air space should be between the two walls.

■ fill existing hollow-core concrete blocks with poured concrete or with polyvinyl chloride pipes (with sealed end caps) full of water to increase thermal storage mass of wall. (Do not fill cores with sand or stones because there is a great deal of dead air space between individual granules and stones.)

■ fill dead air space between double-thick south-facing brick wall with poured concrete *if* the wall is structurally sound and is to be used for thermal storage mass. Fill air space in east, west, and north walls with insulation material (blown or poured) and/or insulate outside of wall.

■ remove interior insulation from existing south-facing masonry walls used for Trombe walls or attached solar additions, sunspaces, and greenhouses.

■ remove carpeting from concrete slab floors struck by direct or reflected sunlight; paint

(or stain) floor medium-dark to dark color or cover with quarry tile or dark brick. (Use area rugs on new floor, but do not cover more than 30 percent of it.)
- consider unusual or innovative ways to provide heat storage mass, such as oversized flowerpots, bookcases that include water containers, or brick-topped window seats.

VENTILATION AND HEAT DISTRIBUTION OPENINGS

FOR VENTILATION <u>LOCATE</u>

- roof wind turbines, operable skylights, roof windows, attic fans, power roof vents, awning windows, and other such devices in roof or high on wall of house, greenhouse, sunspaces, or Trombe walls to allow hot air to escape during the cooling season and set up "stack effect," which will draw cooler air through lower vent openings or windows and screen doors.
- low vents (louvered vents, awning windows, screen doors) on side of house that faces prevailing summer breezes; high vents (windows, sliding glass doors, skylights, roof vents) on opposite side of house. (Increasing the height between intake and exhaust openings increases the velocity of airflow); or
- low vents on north, shaded side of house where the air near the ground is cooler because it is usually in the shade.

FOR HEAT DISTRIBUTION <u>LOCATE</u>

- high and low thermosiphoning vents between attached solar collectors (greenhouse,

sunspace, solar porch, TAPs, Trombe walls, waterwalls) and living spaces; allow at least 6 feet (1.8 m) between high and low vents. Existing or added windows and sliding glass doors can also serve as vents if they allow adequate airflow. A sliding glass door is particularly effective, since the top of the opening admits hot air to the living space, while the bottom of the opening serves as a return for cold air. The space between the moving air at the top and bottom is essentially stagnant.
- back-draft dampers on high and low vents to prevent cool air from collector areas (Trombe walls, waterwalls, TAPs) from entering the living space at night during the heating season. These can be as simple as a flap made of polyethylene film taped over wire mesh or 1/8-inch (.31-cm) hardware cloth.
- registers, air plenums, grills, and cutouts between interior walls and floors to allow air to flow freely throughout living spaces.
- variable-speed, electrically reversible, paddle blade ceiling fans or air destratification jets at the top of living spaces to prevent heated air from stagnating at the ceiling level during the heating season. These can also aid in cooling the space in summer.

SIZE HEATING AND VENTILATION OPENINGS

- outlet vents in the living space (windows, screen doors, operable skylights, etc.) should have a total area that is larger than inlet vents. This is especially true in humid climates. Inlet and outlet vents should be of approximately equal total area in less humid or dry climates.
- upper vents between a greenhouse or sunspace and adjoining living space should total about 9 percent of the floor area of the greenhouse or sunspace. Lower vents should total about 6 percent of the floor area of the greenhouse or sunspace. High and low vents

should have a vertical distance of at least 6 feet (1.8 m) between them.

- high and low summer cooling vents from attached greenhouse, sunspace, or solar addition to outdoors should total approximately 15 percent of the floor area of the greenhouse, sunspace, or solar addition.
- upper and lower thermosiphoning vents between a one-story Trombe wall and adjoining living space should total about 1 percent of the total area of the Trombe wall surface. Vents in a two-story Trombe wall should be about 2 percent of the wall surface.
- upper thermosiphoning vents between a waterwall and adjoining living space should total about 6 percent of the total area of south-facing glazing covering the waterwall. Lower vents should total about 4 percent of the south glazing area.

SIZE SHADING OVERHANGS

- use the chart in figure B-1 to calculate the horizontal projection of overhangs to shade glazing areas.

ADAPT HEATING AND VENTILATION OPENINGS

- use unvented Trombe wall for rooms not normally used during the daytime.
- consider using low-volume (quiet) fans at the ceiling level of attached solar-heated space to direct excess heat to living spaces or thermal storage mass. This is preferable to wasting the heat by allowing the solar space to overheat or venting it to the outdoors in winter.
- plant shrubbery near low intake vents used for summer cooling.
- for ventilation purposes use windows that open fully (for example, awning, transom, casement, horizontally or vertically pivoting-type windows).

B-1. Shade Determination Chart

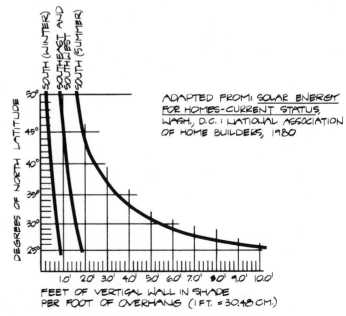

ADAPTED FROM: SOLAR ENERGY FOR HOMES-CURRENT STATUS, WASH., D.C.: NATIONAL ASSOCIATION OF HOME BUILDERS, 1980

USED WITH PERMISSION OF THE NATIONAL ASSOCIATION OF HOME BUILDERS, 15th & M STS., N.W.; WASH., D.C. 20005

HOW TO SIZE SHADING OVERHANGS

To determine the appropriate size for fixed overhangs to shade glazing that faces south (180°), southeast (135°), or southwest (225°), first find the approximate latitude for your location on the left column of the chart in figure B-1. (Refer to figure 2-8 to find your latitude.) Follow the latitude line across the chart until it intersects with the heavy curved line that represents the season and the orientation of the glazing you want to shade. Project a vertical line downward from the point where the latitude line and the heavy curved line meet; then read the scale at the bottom of the chart to determine how many feet of vertical wall surface will be in shade for each foot (.31 m) of overhang.

Example

Indianapolis, Indiana, is located at approximately 40° north latitude. If you wanted to determine how far an overhang should extend horizontally above a south-facing window so the window would be shaded in summer, you would follow the 40° line to the point where it crosses the heavy curved line marked "South (Summer)." Projecting downward from the intersection of the 40° latitude line and the "South (Summer)" curve, you will find that each foot (.31 m) of overhang above a south-facing window will shade about 2.4 feet, or 28 $\frac{4}{5}$ inches (73.15 cm), of vertical wall surface in summer. If, for example, the *bottom* of an existing south window is located about 78 inches (198 cm) below the underside of a 36-inch (91-cm) overhang, that window would be in shade during the summer. To determine if part of a window will be shaded during the winter by a 36-inch (91-cm) overhang, return to the chart and project a line downward from the point where the 40° latitude line and the heavy line marked "South (Winter)" intersect. Projecting downward from this intersection, you could estimate that approximately .5 feet, or 6 inches (15.24 cm), of the south wall would be shaded during the winter by each foot (.31 m) of overhang. Therefore, the *top* of a south window in a house located at 40° north latitude should be located 18 inches (45.72 cm) *below* a 36-inch (91-cm) overhang. (If the window is placed higher on the wall, the top portion of the window will be shaded during the winter by a 36-inch (91-cm) overhang.)

If you begin by measuring the horizontal projection of the existing overhangs on the eaves of your house, you can use the chart to determine how much of the glazing will be in shade during summer *and* winter. Since the overhangs on your house were probably not sized according to these procedures, it may be necessary to adjust the horizontal projection of the overhangs, either by extending the overhang with a trellis or other fixed or movable shading device, or by reducing their horizontal projection by cutting them back or notching them above the windows.

Appendix C: Subcontractor's Agreement Form

The following form is an example of a legal agreement that may be used in working with subcontractors who may be helping you with your retrofit project. You will find that taking the time to use this—or a similar contract—may help prevent some possible problems.

SUBCONTRACT AGREEMENT

THIS AGREEMENT, made this_____day of_____19____, by and between_____
hereinafter called the Owner/Contractor, and_____ hereinafter called the
Subcontractor.

    For the consideration hereinafter named, the said Subcontractor covenants and agrees with said Owner/
Contractor, as follows:

    1. The Subcontractor agrees to (furnish all material and) perform all work necessary to complete the

_____

_____

for the above-named structure, according to the plans and specifications (details thereof to be furnished as
needed) and to the full satisfaction of Owner.

    2. The Subcontractor agrees to promptly begin said work as soon as notified by said Owner/Contractor,
and to complete the work as follows:_____

_____

_____

_____

_____

    3. The Subcontractor shall take out and pay for Workmen's Compensation and Public Liability Insurance,
also Property Damage and all other necessary insurance, as required by the Owner/Contractor or by the
State in which this work is performed.

    4. The Subcontractor shall pay all Sales Taxes, Old Age Benefit and Unemployment Compensation
Taxes upon the (material and) labor furnished under this contract, as required by the United States Government and the State in which this work is performed.

    5. No extra work or changes under this contract will be recognized or paid for unless agreed to in
writing before the work is done or the changes made.

    6. This contract shall not be assigned by the Subcontractor without first obtaining permission in writing
from the Owner/Contractor.

IN CONSIDERATION WHEREOF, the said Owner/Contractor agrees that he will pay to said Subcontractor
the sum of ($_____)_____Dollars for above (materials and) work, to
be paid as follows:_____percent (_____%) of all labor (and materials) that have been placed in
position by said Subcontractor and balance_____

_____

_____

_____

until paid in full, after said Subcontractor has completed his work to the full satisfaction of all parties
concerned, i.e.,   Owner/Contractor   Designer/Architect. If requested, Subcontractor agrees to furnish
Owner/Contractor with Waiver of Lien for materials and labor.

    The Owner/Contractor and the Subcontractor for themselves, their successors, executors, administrators
and assigns, hereby agree to the full performance of the covenants of this agreement.

    IN WITNESS WHEREOF, this agreement has been executed on the day and date written above.

_____   _____
         (Witness)   (Owner/Contractor)

_____   _____
         (Witness)   (Subcontractor)

Appendix D: Directory of Natural Resources

SELECTED BIBLIOGRAPHY

Listed below, by category, is a collection of recommended books and magazines that you may find useful for further reading or study. (Ordering information is included for some of the more difficult-to-locate items.)

FUNDAMENTALS AND FOUNDATIONS OF PASSIVE SOLAR

Augustyn, Jim. *The Solar Cat Book.* Berkeley, CA: Ten Speed Press, 1979. (Available from: Ten Speed Press, P.O. Box 7123, Berkeley, CA 94707.)

Baer, Steven. *Sunspots.* 3rd ed. Albuquerque, NM: Zomeworks Corp., 1980.

Wright, David. *Natural Solar Architecture: A Passive Primer.* New York: Van Nostrand Reinhold Co., 1978.

DESIGNING, PLANNING, AND DRAWING (GENERAL)

Ching, Francis. *Building Construction Illustrated.* New York: Van Nostrand Reinhold Co., 1975.

Curran, June. *Drawing House Plans: A Simplified Drafting System for Planning and Design.* Bakersfield, CA: Brooks Publishing Co., 1979.

DiDonno, Lupe and Sperling, Phyllis. *How to Design and Build Your Own Home.* New York: Alfred A. Knopf, 1980.

Lamb, Charles. *Homestyles.* New York: St. Martin's Press, 1979.

McLaughlin, Jack. *The Housebuilding Experience.* New York: Van Nostrand Reinhold Co., 1981.

Moore, Charles, et al. *The Place of Houses.* New York: Holt, Rinehart and Winston, 1979.

Walker, Les and Milsten, Jeff. *Designing Houses: An Illustrated Guide to Building Your Own House.* Woodstock, NY: The Overlook Press, 1976.

PASSIVE SOLAR DESIGN HANDBOOKS (TECHNICAL)

Balcomb, J. Douglas, et al. (Los Alamos Scientific Laboratory). *Passive Solar Design Analysis.* Passive Solar Design Handbook, Vol. 2. Washington, DC: U.S. Department of Energy, 1980. (Available from: National Technical Information Service, 5285 Port Royal Road, Springfield, VA 22151. Document# DOE/CS-0127/2; $14.00.)

Lewis, Daniel, et al. (Total Environment Action, Inc.). *Passive Solar Design Concepts.* Passive Solar Design Handbook, Vol. 1. Washington, DC: U.S. Department of Energy, 1980. (Available from: National Technical Information Service, 5285 Port Royal Road, Springfield, VA 22151. Document# DOE/CS-0127/1; $13.25.)

Niles, Philip and Haggard, Kenneth L. *Passive Solar Handbook.* Sacramento, CA: California Energy Commission, 1980. (Available from: California Energy Commission, Solar Office, 1111 Howe Avenue, Sacramento, CA 95825; $10.00.)

Total Environmental Action. *The Thermal Mass Pattern Book.* Harrisville, NH: Total Environmental Action, Inc., 1980. (Available from: TEA, Inc., Harrisville, NH 03450; $1.25)

Wilson, Alex. *Thermal Storage Wall Design Manual.* Santa Fe: New Mexico Solar Energy Association, 1979. (Available from: NMSEA, P.O. Box 2004, Santa Fe, NM 87501; $4.00.)

PASSIVE SOLAR DESIGN (NONTECHNICAL)

Anderson, Bruce and Wells, Malcolm. *Passive Solar Energy.* Andover, MA: Brick House Publishing Co., 1981.

Bainbridge, David A. *The Second Passive Solar Catalog.* Davis, CA: The Passive Solar Institute, 1980. (Available from: The Passive Solar Institute, P.O. Box 722, Davis, CA 95616; $12.50 ppd.)

Mazria, Edward. *The Passive Solar Energy Book.* Emmaus, PA: Rodale Press, 1979.

Wilson, Tom, ed. *Home Remedies: A Guidebook for Residential Retrofit.* Philadelphia: Mid-Atlantic Solar Energy Association, 1981. (Available from MASEA, 2233 Gray's Ferry Avenue, Philadelphia, PA 19146; $10.00.)

Wright, Rodney, et al. (the Hawkweed Group). *Passive Solar House Book.* Chicago: Rand McNally & Co., 1980.

PASSIVE SOLAR CONSTRUCTION (HOW-TO BOOKS)

Owner Builder Center. *Build Your Own House.* Berkeley, CA: Ten Speed Press, 1982. (Available from Ten Speed Press, P.O. Box 7123, Berkeley, CA 94707.)

Passive Solar Construction Handbook. Atlanta: Southern Solar Energy Center, 1981. (Available from: Southern Solar Energy Center, 61 Perimeter Park, Atlanta, GA 30341; $20.00.)

Passive Retrofit Handbook: Solar Applications for Residences. Atlanta: Southern Solar Energy Center, 1981. (Available from: Southern Solar Energy Center, 61 Perimeter Park, Atlanta, GA 30341; $10.00.)

Reif, Daniel K. *Solar Retrofit: Adding Solar to Your Home.* Andover, MA: Brick House Publishing Co., 1981.

Schwolsky, Rick and Williams, James. *The Builders' Guide to Solar Construction.* New York: McGraw-Hill, 1982.

Wing, Charles. *From the Walls In.* Boston: Little, Brown and Co., 1979.

Yanda, Bill and Fisher, Rick. *The Food and Heat Producing Greenhouse.* Santa Fe: John Muir Publications, Inc., 1980. (Available from: John Muir Publications, Inc., P.O. Box 613, Santa Fe, NM 87501; $9.00 ppd.)

MOVABLE INSULATION

Langdon, William. *Movable Insulation*. Emmaus, PA: Rodale Press, 1980.

Shurcliff, William. *Thermal Shutters and Shades*. Andover, MA: Brick House Publishing Co., 1980.

Wolf, Ray. *Insulating Window Shade*. Emmaus, PA: Rodale Press, 1980.

WEATHER DATA

Climatic Atlas of the United States. Washington, DC: U.S. Department of Commerce, 1968. (Available from: National Climatic Center Publications, Federal Building, Asheville, NC 28801; $6.00 ppd.)

Local Climatological Data. Washington, DC: U.S. Department of Commerce. (Available from: National Climatic Center Publications, Federal Building, Asheville, NC 28801; yearly subscription, $3.30—includes monthly and yearly summaries for National Weather Service Office locations.)

MAGAZINES

The Mother Earth News
    105 Stoney Mountain Road
    Hendersonville, NC 28739
    ($12.00/yr; 6 issues)

New Shelter
    33 East Minor Street
    Emmaus, PA 18049
    ($9.00/yr; 9 issues)

In addition, *Mechanix Illustrated, Popular Science, Sunset, Better Homes and Gardens,* and *Family Handyman* sometimes feature articles or plans related to passive solar retrofits.

PASSIVE SOLAR PRODUCT MANUFACTURERS

The addresses of manufacturers listed below should help you locate the materials you need to complete your retrofit project. Write or call the manufacturers to find out about the cost and availability of their products in your area.

GLAZING

Exolite™ (double-skinned acrylic or polycarbonate sheets)
    CY/RO Industries
    Bound Brook, NJ 08805
    (201) 356–2000

Sunlite™ and Sunwall™ (fiberglass-reinforced polyester glazing)
    Kalwall Corporation
    Solar Components Division
    P.O. Box 237
    Manchester, NH 03105
    (603) 668–8186

Filon™ (fiberglass-reinforced polyester glazing)
    Vistron Corporation, Filon Division
    12333 Van Ness Avenue
    Hawthorne, CA 90250
    (213) 757–5141

Solakleer™ (low-iron flat glass)
    General Glass International Corporation
    270 North Avenue
    New Rochelle, NY 10801
    (914) 235–5900

Sunadex™ and Lo-iron™ (tempered transparent glass)
    ASG Industries
    P.O. Box 929
    Kingsport, TN 37662
    (615) 245–0211

OPERABLE ROOF WINDOWS AND SKYLIGHTS

Velux™ (Roof Windows)
Velux-America, Inc.
74 Cummings Park
Woburn, MA 01801
(617) 935–7390

902 Morse Avenue
Schaumburg, IL 60193
(312) 894–1002

3520 Progress Drive
I-95 Industrial Center
Cornwells Heights, PA 19020
(215) 245–1140

4725 Nautilus Court South
Boulder, CO 80301
(303) 530–1698

Ventarama™ (skylights)
Ventarama Skylight Corporation
75 Channel Drive
Port Washington, NY 11050
(516) 883–5000

84 Broadway
Somerville, MA 02145
(617) 628–8210

THERMAL STORAGE

Freestanding Water Containers

Fiberglass Water Tubes
Waterwall Engineering
Route 1, Box 6
New Paris, OH 45347
(513) 437–7261

Kalwall™ Storage Tubes
Kalwall Corporation
Solar Components Division
P.O. Box 237
Manchester, NH 03105
(603) 668–8186

Integral Waterwall Containers

Tubewall™ and Tankwall™
Waterwall Engineering
Route 1, Box 6
New Paris, OH 45347
(513) 437–7261

Stud Space Module™
One Design, Inc.
Mountain Falls Route
Winchester, VA 22601
(703) 877–2172

Heat Wall™
Suncraft
5001 East 59th Street
Kansas City, MO 64130
(816) 333–2100

Selective Surface Coating

SunSponge™
Berry Solar Products
Box 327
Edison, NJ 08817
(201) 549–3800

Phase Change Materials (PCM)

Rods

SCM Energy Rod™
Certified Energy Systems, Inc.
24147 Juanita
San Jacinto, CA 92383
(714) 654–0895

Thermalrod-27™
Energy Materials, Inc.
2622 South Zuni Street
Englewood, CO 80110
(303) 934–2444

Thermol 81—The Energy Rod™
PSI Energy Systems, Inc.
15331 Fen Park Drive
St. Louis (Fenton), MO 63026
(314) 343–7666

Pods and Packs

Kalwall Solar-Pod™
  Kalwall Corporation
  Solar Components Division
  P.O. Box 237
  Manchester, NH 03105
  (603) 668–8186

Heat Pac™
  Colloridal Materials, Inc.
  P.O. Box 696
  Andover, MA 01810
  (617) 475–3276

Floor Tiles

Sol-ar-tile™
  Architectural Research Corporation
  13030 Wayne Road
  Livonia, MI 48150
  (313) 525–9400

Cans

Texxor Heat Cells™
  Texxor Corporation
  9910 North 48th Street
  Omaha, NE 68152
  (402) 453–7558

INSULATION

Roll-down Insulating Shades

Insulating Curtain Wall™ (multilayer insulating/reflective shades)
  Thermal Technology Corporation
  P.O. Box 130
  Snowmass, CO 81654
  (303) 963–3185

Insulating Shade (multilayer insulating shades)
  Insulating Shade Company, Inc.
  P.O. Box 282
  Branford, CT 06405
  (203) 481–2337

The Window Manager™ (multilayer insulating/reflective shades)
  Star Shade
  Star Technology Corporation
  417 Main Street
  Carbondale, CO 81623
  (303) 963–1969

Window Quilt™ (quilted insulating shades)
  Appropriate Technology Corporation
  P.O. Box 975
  Brattleboro, VT 05301
  (802) 257–4501

Insulated Shutters

Wovoak™ Insulated Shutters (woven-wood insulating shutters)
  Wovoak
  5725 Arapahoe Avenue
  Boulder, CO 80303
  (303) 449–7893

Insul Shutter™ (insulated wooden shutters for doors and windows)
  Insul Shutter, Inc.
  P.O. Box 338
  Silt, CO 81652
  (303) 876–2743

Insulated Folding Shutters (hinged folding insulated shutters for windows and doors)
  Shutters, Inc.
  110 East Fifth Street
  Hastings, MN 55033
  (612) 437–2566

Skylid™, Breadwall™, Nightwall Clips™ (and other insulating shutters, plans, and accessories)
  Zomeworks Corporation
  P.O. Box 712
  Albuquerque, NM 87103
  (505) 242–5354

Masonry Insulation Systems

Exterior Insulation for Masonry Walls (stucco over styrofoam finishes)

Dryvit Outsulation™
Dryvit Systems, Inc.
420 Lincoln Avenue
Warwick, RI 02888
(401) 463–7150

Settef System™
Compo Industries, Inc.
Chemical Specialties Group
125 Roberts Road
Waltham, MA 02154
(617) 899–3000

Integrated Insulating Systems (for poured concrete; insulation is integrated within the pour)

Thermocurve™
Thermocurve, Inc.
P.O. Box 205
Fishers, IN 46038
(317) 849–6350

Form Foam™
Insul-Crete Building Systems, Inc.
777 Woodstock Road
Quechee, VT 05059
(802) 295–9555

AIR DISTRIBUTION

Self-Operating Vent Openers

Series 35 Thermal Operator™ and Solarvent™
Dalen Products, Inc.
201 Sherlake Drive
Knoxville, TN 37922
(615) 690–0050

Heat Motor™
Heat Motors Distributing
P.O. Box 411
Fair Oaks, CA 95628
(916) 967–0859

Thermofor™
Bramen Company, Inc.
P.O. Box 70
Salem, MA 01970
(616) 745–7765

Air Destratification Jets

Strato-Jet™ and Stratotherm™
Rusth Industries
P.O. Box 1519
Beaverton, OR 97005
(503) 644–2582

PASSIVE SOLAR WATER HEATING

Plans for Breadbox Water Heaters

Integral Design
3825 Sebastopol Road
Santa Rosa, CA 95401

Mother's Plans
The Mother Earth News
P.O. Box 70
Hendersonville, NC 28739

Passive Solar Institute
P.O. Box 722
Davis, CA 95616

Solstice Publications
P.O. Box 2043
Evergreen, CO 80439
(do-it-yourself plans for breadbox water heater and other passive solar devices)

Sunspace, Inc.
P.O. Box 172
Ada, OK 74820
(plans for prism-shaped water heater shown in fig. 3-26; $2.00 ppd.)

Tennessee Valley Authority
Division of Energy Conservation
Solar Applications Branch
Chattanooga, TN 37401
(TVA Sunbox™)

Zomeworks Corporation
P.O. Box 712
Albuquerque, NM 87103

Tanks for Breadbox Water Heaters

American Appliance
2341 Michigan Avenue
Santa Monica, CA 90404
(203) 829–1755

Kalwall Corporation
Solar Components Division
P.O. Box 237
Manchester, NH 03105
(603) 668–8186

Preassembled Breadbox Water Heater

EPI Energy Systems
1424 West 259th Street
Harbor City, CA 90710
(213) 539–8590

Collector Fins

Big Fin™
Zomeworks Corporation
P.O. Box 712
Albuquerque, NM 87103
(505) 242–5354

Little Fin™
Colorado Sunworks
959 Walnut Street
Boulder, CO 80306
(303) 443–9199

Passive Hot Water Systems

Soltec Hot Water™
Solar Technology Corporation
2160 Clay Street
Denver, CO 80211
(303) 455–3309

PREFABRICATED GREENHOUSES, SOLARIA, AND SUNSPACES

Garden Way Solar Greenhouse
Garden Way Research
Charlotte, VT 05445
(802) 425–2137

Habitat Solar Room™
Habitat Specialty Buildings, Inc.
123 Elm Street
South Deerfield, MA 01373
(413) 665–4006

Solar Room Kit
Solar Resources, Inc.
P.O. Box 1848
Taos, NM 87571
(505) 758–9344

Soltec Greenroom™
Solar Technology Corporation
2160 Clay Street
Denver, CO 80211
(303) 455–3309

Sturdi-built Solar Greenhouses
Sturdi-built Manufacturing Company
11304 Boones Ferry Road, SW
Portland, OR 97219
(503) 244–4100

Sunglo Solar Greenhouses
Sunglo Greenhouses
4441 26th Avenue, West
Seattle, WA 98199
(206) 284–8900

Sun Haus™
Weather Energy Systems, Inc.
39 Barlows Landing Road
Pocasset, MA 02559
(617) 563–9337

The Sunspace
Northern Sun
21705 Highway 99
Lynnwood, WA 98036
(206) 771–3334

Sunwrights Sun-Kit
Sunwrights
1798 Massachusetts Avenue
Cambridge, MA 02140
(617) 547–0330

PREFABRICATED (OR PREASSEMBLED) THERMOSIPHONING AIR PANELS (TAPs)

Free Heat BTU Bank™ (installs under south-facing window)
Solar Bank, Inc.
5600 Roswell Road, NE
Suite 290, Prado East
Atlanta, GA 30342
(404) 252–5036

Heliopass™ 100 (passive TAP)
Independent Energies, Inc.
Route 131, Box 398
Schoolcraft, MI 49087
(616) 344–7943

Isis Solar Heater™ (fan-assisted TAP)
Solar Futures, Inc.
P.O. Box 7998
Louisville, KY 40207
(812) 945–8419

Passive Solar Heat Wall™ (TAP with thermal storage)
Crimsco, Inc.
5001 East 59th Street
Kansas City, MO 64130
(816) 333–2100

Sunway Wall Collector™ (fan-assisted TAP)
Sunway Corporation
P.O. Box 9723
Pittsburgh, PA 15229
(412) 364–5349

OWNER-BUILDER SCHOOLS

The owner-builder schools listed below offer hands-on training programs for designing and building (or remodeling) homes based on energy-efficient, passive solar principles. Write or call for information on their programs.

Cornerstones
54 Cumberland Street
Brunswick, ME 04011
(207) 729–0540

Going Solar
216 Canyon Acres Drive
Laguna Beach, CA 92651
(714) 494–9341

Heartwood Owner-Builder School
Johnson Road
Washington, MA 01235
(413) 623–6677

Northern Owner Builder
RD #1
Plainfield, VT 05667
(802) 454–7808

Owner Builder Center
1824 Fourth Street
Berkeley, CA 94710
(415) 848–5951

Shelter Institute
38 Center Street
Bath, ME 04530
(207) 442–7938

Sunrise Builders School
Route 121
Grafton, VT 05146
(802) 843–2285

Acknowledgments

Although mine is the only name that appears as the author on the title page of this book, many people in fact contributed to the development of the manuscript. This book could not have been completed without the assistance, advice, support, and encouragement of numerous individuals and organizations.

I would like to express my sincere appreciation to the following people and groups for the help they provided. Gratitude is expressed to

the solar designers whose work appears in this book: J. Douglas and Sara Balcomb, Passive Solar Associates; H. Nelson Blue, Solar Gardens; Terry Egnor, Ecotope Group; Rollin Francisco, Rainshadow Design; Doug Kellbaugh, Kellbaugh & Lee Associates; Carl Lehrburger, Solar Technology Corporation; Paul Luther, PRADO; Tim Magee, Rainshadow Design; F. Eugene Metz, National Bureau of Standards; Peter J. Pfister, Architectural Alliance; Donald Schramm, PRADO; Rachel Snyder, Infinite Energy; Mike Verway, The Solar Project; Ron Wolf, Sunspace Construction Company; Peggy Wrenn, Colorado Office of Energy Conservation; Bill and Susan Yanda, Sunplace Corporation; Bill Zoellick, Sunspace, Inc.;

to the organizations that provided much useful information and, in some cases, photographs: The Center for Ecological Technology, Pittsfield, MA; The Solar Project, Lancaster, PA; *The Mother Earth News,* Hendersonville, NC; The National Solar Heating and Cooling Information Center, Rockville, MD; Tennessee Valley Authority, Solar Applications Branch, Chattanooga, TN; National Climatic Center, Asheville, NC; Internal Revenue Service, Washington, DC;

to Bruce M. Bolme, Physical Engineer, and Akira Kawanabe, Solar Architect, who reviewed the "Guidelines for Passive Solar Design" in Appendix B and provided expert technical advice;

to the photographers whose works appear herein: Franz C. Hall, Carrie Hendron, Phares O'Daffer, Robert Perron, Steve Solinsky, David S. Strickler, Joe Wilkinson, and Harriet Wise;

to architectural designer/draftsman/illustrator par excellence, Rossetti Perchick, whose technical drawings appear among the illustrations in this book;

164

to the patient and competent people who typed the manuscript for this book: Helen Frisbie and Marcie Sugg;

to Barbara Ravage of Van Nostrand Reinhold, editor, content critic, general encourager, and "which-hunter," who changed many "whichs" to "thats," "cans" to "mays," and placed the "howevers" where they really belong—and much, much more—all of *which* resulted in a better book *that may* be more readable in the long run;

to Dr. P. L. Gaither, friend, partner, advisor, motivator, and agent, who was instrumental in getting the project started, saw it through to completion, and provided much invaluable assistance, support, encouragement, and understanding along the way;

to Dr. B. P. Farr, friend, counselor, and general support person, who reviewed the proposal for the book and provided a great deal of encouragement to begin the project and keep it going;

to D. Leon Ragsdale, architect, master teacher, and spiritual leader, who provided many new insights and who reviewed the complete manuscript and suggested many helpful improvements;

to Zeen Cummins, all-around terrific person, who joined the effort late but made up for the late start by seeing to it that the project was completed on time and in good order;

to my mother, my brothers and sisters (all nine of them), my in-laws, outlaws, nieces and nephews (all fifty of them)—a group of first-rate people who among them own enough retrofittable houses to make this book worthwhile even if no one else buys it;

and finally, but most importantly, to Lauren, Kyle, Derek, Cody, and Kristin, sons, daughters, and little friends, who provided the real reasons to write this book in the first place.

Index

F

G

H

I

About the Author

Darryl Strickler writes about passive solar retrofits from a position of experience. He has designed numerous retrofits, as well as new passive solar homes, in various parts of the country. His most important qualification to write this book, however, is his own experience in rebuilding an aging concrete block house and transforming it into a passive solar home with a zero heating and cooling bill.

Dr. Strickler is a solar design professional, educator, author, and designer/producer of instructional television programs. In addition to operating a solar design service, he teaches courses and conducts workshops on passive solar retrofitting and works with community and school groups. He began his studies in the field of architectural engineering and design in 1960. After completing his bachelor's and master's degrees, he taught for several years before completing his doctorate at the State University of New York at Buffalo in 1972.

For seven years he was a faculty member at Indiana University, where he taught graduate and undergraduate courses, conducted research studies, and produced educational television programs. He left his job at the university to devote his time to solar design work, writing, lecturing, and television productions relating to passive solar applications for home heating and cooling.